W9-BHV-475

CREATIVE CRUCIVERBALISTS

CREATIVE CRUCIVERBALISTS

Those Curious Crossword Creators and Their Best Puzzles

HELENE HOVANEC

QUILL
William Morrow
New York

All photographs by Joe Hovanec

Grateful acknowledgment is made for permission to use the following:

Puzzles:

Heller: Reprinted courtesy of Publications International, Ltd.
Jacobson: Copyright © 1981 by Maura Jacobson
Lasher: Reprinted courtesy of *The Boston Globe*
Maleska: Copyright © 1974 by Simon & Schuster, Inc. Reprinted by permission of Simon & Schuster, Inc.
Newman: Copyright © 1985 by American Crossword Federation
Reagle: Copyright © 1985 by Merl Reagle

Cartoons on page 22 copyright © by J. B. R. Inc. Used with permission.

Library of Congress Cataloging-in-Publication Data

Hovanec, Helene, 1941–
  Creative cruciverbalists.
  1. Crossword puzzles. 2. Crossword puzzle makers—
Biography. I. Title.
GV1507.C7H685 1988 793.73′2′0922 [B] 87-7278
ISBN 0-688-06578-3

Printed in the United States of America

First Edition

1 2 3 4 5 6 7 8 9 10

BOOK DESIGN BY BERNARD SCHLEIFER

CONTENTS

Contents

To the memory of Margaret Farrar

INTRODUCTION

I WAS IMMOBILE during the summer of 1985. I had ignored the old maxim to let sleeping dogs lie and had tripped over my dachshund as he was snoozing on the steps. I tumbled clumsily down four steps and landed inelegantly on my ankle. I could almost hear the bone crack. When the orthopedist put my leg in a cast for six weeks, I knew I had to take up a project or I'd drive myself and my family crazy bemoaning my fate.

So I started to solve crossword puzzles with a passion. I've been a puzzle person since I was six years old, but I had never before solved so many puzzles in such a short time. I've also been active in the puzzle world for a dozen years—as a judge at most of the modern puzzle tournaments, coordinator of four conventions for the National Puzzlers' League, editor of puzzle magazines, and author of several puzzle books.

As I went through book after book of crosswords I thought about the people behind the by-lines. Most of them were my friends or, at the very least, my acquaintances. I thought that a book profiling these master wordsmiths would be interesting to aficionados addicted to the world of black and white grids who wanted to know more about the constructors behind creative crosswords.

The constructors profiled here are all erudite, witty people whose puzzles create joy and/or havoc for millions of crossword fans throughout the country. I've derived pleasure from their puzzles through the years and hope you'll enjoy meeting the people behind the by-lines.

BACK TO SQUARE ONE

IN 1921 MARGARET PETHERBRIDGE, a young Smith College graduate hired by *The New York World* as a secretary, had nothing but scorn for the crossword puzzle:

"The checkered square, with its columns of definitions, was unsightly, had no decorative value, and was published, as a sort of necessary nuisance, in the obscurest corner of the paper. No one in the office ever dreamed of amusing himself by working out one of the strange-looking constructions, or even bothered to inquire about the rules of the ridiculous game."

Harsh words indeed, coming as they did from someone who later became, under her married name of Farrar, the doyenne of the crossword-puzzle world for sixty years.

The puzzle itself had made its debut inauspiciously on December 21, 1913. *The New York World*'s Fun Page editor, Arthur Wynne, was determined to introduce a new variety of puzzle for the Christmas issue. Using an old idea, the word square, he expanded and refined it to create his first "Word-Cross Puzzle."

Word squares, in which the same words read both across and down, date back to the first century with the palindromic Sator acrostic:

R O T A S
O P E R A
T E N E T
A R E P O
S A T O R

This word square, which roughly translates into "Arepo, the sower, carefully guides the wheels" or "God controls the universe," was believed to have magical properties. It was a relatively simple word form compared to the stele of Moschion, a thirty-nine-inch alabaster square dating from the second or third century. The phrase "Moschion to Osiris, for the treatment which cured his foot" is repeated over and over. Moschion's way of honoring the god Osiris is an excellent example of the lengths to which constructors have gone to please their audiences.

It wasn't until 1862, however, that the word square was introduced in America with this square published in *Godey's Lady's Book:*

C I R C L E
I C A R U S
R A R E S T
C R E A T E
L U S T R E
E S T E E M

For the *World*'s fun page, Arthur Wynne altered the square in several ways. He used different words across and down, set them into a diamond shape, and inserted numbers in some of the boxes. He then defined each entry and indicated its place in the grid with a two-numeral system.

Wynne positioned his Word-Cross prominently in the top center of the puzzle page with terse instructions to "Fill in the small squares with words which agree with the following definitions." Surrounded by riddles (Q: "What word is shorter when you add one syllable to it?" A: "Short."), jokes ("We had four blowouts on the road last night."—"Your car must be awfully tired.") and magic tricks, it was a rather humble beginning for what would ultimately become the world's most popular puzzle.

Printed without fanfare, the puzzle won immediate reader interest: Several people responded by sending in constructions of their own. It was all the impetus Wynne needed to publish a second puzzle, along with the answers to the first, commenting that "the great interest in FUN's word-cross puzzle has prompted the puzzle editor to submit another of the same kind."

For the next few weeks, Wynne's cross-words (the original name was soon transposed) appeared regularly on Sundays. On February 1, 1914, Wynne obliquely solicited contributions: "FUN's cross-word puzzles apparently are getting more popular than ever. The puzzle editor has received from readers many interesting new cross-word puzzles, which he will be glad to use from time to time. It is more difficult to make up a cross-word puzzle than it is to solve one. If you doubt this, try to make one yourself."

Exactly one week later, Mrs. M. B. Wood of New York City

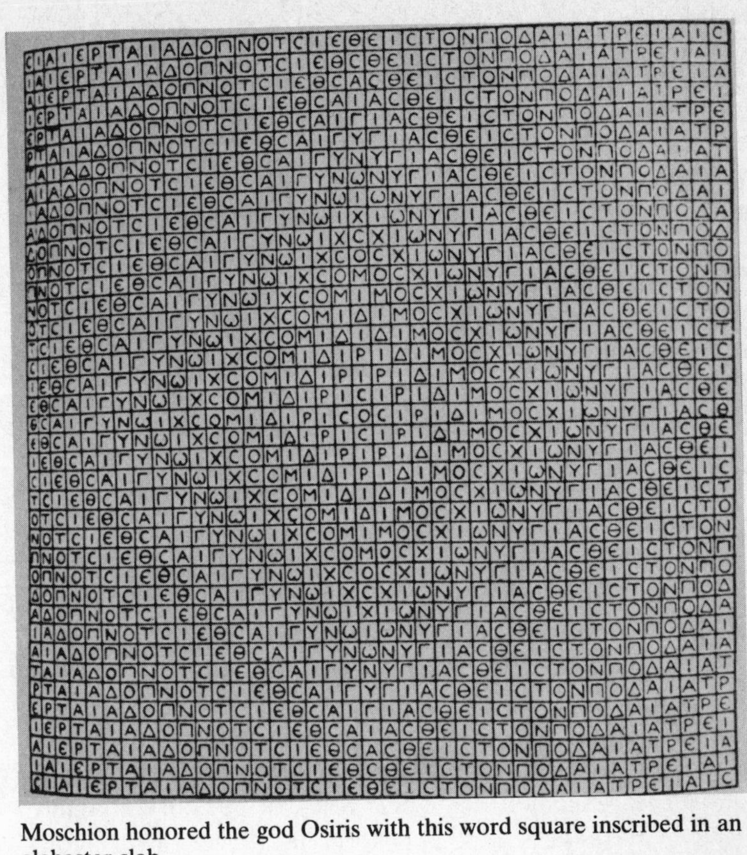

Moschion honored the god Osiris with this word square inscribed in an alabaster slab.

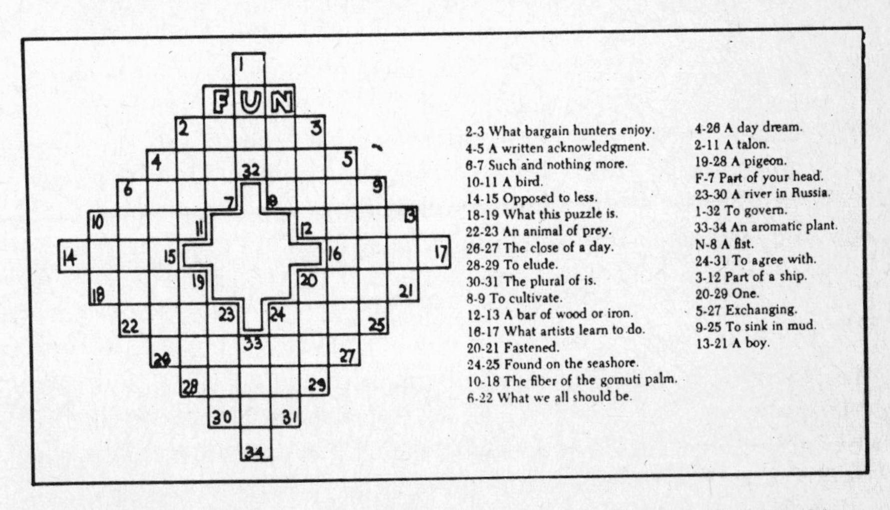

Arthur Wynne's first "word-cross" debuted quietly in *The New York World* on December 21, 1913.

was duly credited as the constructor of Cross-Word #8, thereby achieving a dual feat—she became the first crossword contributor on record and the first one to receive a by-line.

Crosswords continued to come into Wynne's office, and every week a new puzzle appeared exactly as it had been constructed. Then on September 12, 1914, Wynne used some editorial clout by reworking some of the clues in a constructor's puzzle. Thus, Ernest Rust of Yonkers, New York, achieved the dubious distinction of being the first crossword constructor to have his work edited. Wynne explained tactfully that he changed the clues only for the constructor's benefit:

"If the puzzle editor of FUN were to publish it exactly as it was sent in, Mr. Rust would not have any cross-word puzzle to solve this week. So the puzzle editor has taken the great liberty of changing one or two words in Mr. Rust's puzzle in order that he, too, can have an interesting hour or so solving his own puzzle."

Knowing that one's puzzle would be edited didn't scare off potential contributors—puzzles streamed into the *World*. Since they were being published only on Sundays, Wynne acknowledged his problem on March 7, 1915:

"The editor of FUN receives an average of twenty-five cross-word puzzles every day from readers. Considering that only one cross-word is published per week you can possibly imagine what the office of FUN is beginning to look like. Everywhere your eyes rest on boxes, barrels and crates, each one filled with cross-word puzzles patiently awaiting publication. However, the editor of FUN hopes to use them all in time. The puzzle editor has kindly figured it out that the present supply will last until the second week in December, 2100."

During the next few years, crosswords continued to be a fairly regular *World* feature, with a following of loyal and vocal fans. On sporadic occasions when the crossword didn't appear, solvers angrily voiced their objections: "The only thing I give a hang about on your page or in your Sunday magazine is the crossword."

From the outset, however, the puzzle was plagued by typographical errors, misnumbered definitions, omitted clues, and other sloppy work done by disgruntled typographers who didn't like the extra work involved in setting up the crossword. Surprisingly, the puzzles were published without being test-solved first on the page proof.

Typographers' errors made the puzzles so difficult to solve that readers complained bitterly in irate letters. By 1921, an aggravated and tired Arthur Wynne decided to turn the crossword over to someone else. That "someone" turned out to be the newly arrived Margaret Petherbridge, who had been hired as secretary to Sunday editor John O'Hara Cosgrove. Unceremoniously, Cosgrove dumped the crossword into her lap and instructed her to get it into the paper "without mistakes."

Petherbridge had never even seen a crossword when she inherited the editor's job. She chose each week's puzzle solely on esthetic appeal and sent it to the typesetters. Since she didn't solve the puzzles herself, she was able to dismiss solvers' letters of condemnation as "the work of cranks."

But when Franklin Pierce Adams (better known as F.P.A.), creator of the popular "Conning Tower" column, started to badger Petherbridge about the errors, she decided she'd better discover for herself what a puzzle was like. Petherbridge, whose total involvement in crosswords would change them forever, later wrote about her conversion:

"I began by trying to do one the next Sunday, and thus experienced the throes of acute agony that come to all solvers of puzzles on discovering definitions left out, numbers wrong, hideously warped definitions, words not to be found inside of any known dictionary, foreign words—very foreign—and words that had no right to be dragged out of their native obscurity. Then and there, with my left hand reposing on a dictionary and my right raised in air, I took an oath to edit the crosswords to the essence of perfection. From then on, I instituted the procedure of doing the puzzles myself on the page proof—sort of trying it on the dog—applying the principle,

> 'If it be not fair to me,
> What care I how fair it be!' "

Puzzles were now set a week in advance instead of at the last minute, which enabled clues and diagrams to be checked and errors corrected before publication. Other improvements included using dictionary words only, tightening the diagram, eliminating most of the unkeyed letters (those that didn't cross with other letters) and setting up rules for constructors so that the puzzles could become more uniform.

Petherbridge's associates in the editorial department were F. Gregory Hartswick and Prosper Buranelli.

Hartswick, himself a constructor of crosswords, could wax euphoric over the "numerous enjoyments of the crossword":

"There is the pure esthetic stimulation of looking at the pattern with its neat black and white squares, like a floor in a cathedral or a hotel bathroom; there is the challenge of the definitions, titillating the combative ganglion that lurks in all of us; there is the tantalizing elusiveness of the one little word that will satisfactorily fill a space and give clues to others that we know not of; and there is the thrill of triumph as the right word is found, fitted, and its attendant branches and roots spring into being."

Buranelli's knowledge and appreciation of old word puzzles heightened his respect for the crossword. Through his association with the National Puzzlers' League, an erudite group of puzzlers interested in maintaining the status of puzzling as a highly cerebral activity, he was familiar with intricate word forms in the shapes of diamonds, rhomboids, and other geometric figures. He recognized that the crossword was "an expanded word form in which, commonly, only dictionary words are allowed. It is this simplicity of words, together with its larger and more elaborate construction, that makes it irresistible to the casual puzzler. A cross word square, or other geometric figure, is a logical modern development of the ancient word square. The insertion of black spaces permits it to be made of any size and gives an interesting variety of inner construction."

It was Arthur Wynne who had inserted the first black spaces into a geometric form. When, in 1925, Wynne found himself billed as the "Father of the Crossword," he modestly played down his role:

"I awakened recently to find myself acclaimed as the originator of the cross-word puzzle. . . . But unhappily I did not create the cross-word puzzle outright. All I did was take an idea as old as language and modernize it by the introduction of the black squares. But that at least is something and I don't deny my pride in it."

By 1924, the Petherbridge-Buranelli-Hartswick team, using firm editorial guidance, suggestions from intrepid constructors, and native brilliance, had succeeded in shaping the crossword into a most respectable puzzle. Clues were now presented with just a single number (rather than the cumbersome 2-3, 4-5 variety); letters were connected to each other through an overall interlocking pattern; and symmetry prevailed. A regular feature in the Sunday *World,* the crossword was an important part of many lives.

All these improvements notwithstanding, the crossword might have languished were it not for the birth of a new publishing company.

Richard Simon and Max Schuster joined forces in 1924 to create a publishing company bearing their joint names. Graduates of Columbia's School of Journalism, they were searching for a suitable book with with to launch their new business. The legend (later admitted a fabrication) went that Simon's Aunt Wixie suggested that a book of crossword puzzles, such as those found in the *World,* would make an ideal gift for a friend of hers.

Discovering that no such book existed, Simon and Schuster went to the *World*'s offices and persuaded the crossword editors to compile a book of fifty puzzles. Lured by a $75.00 advance (total), the trio drew upon its abundant supply of crosswords and completed the manuscript in record time.

Publication was scheduled for April 10. However, the publishers couldn't seem to interest anyone in their venture and were dubious about starting their business with what would surely be a flop. Cribbing the name of their telephone exchange, they issued *The Cross Word Puzzle Book* under the imprint of the Plaza Publishing Company and printed a modest 3,600 copies. If the book failed, no one need know the publishers' identities.

Six weeks before publication they strategically placed a small ad on the *World's* puzzle page: "Attention, Crossword Puzzle Fans . . . By mail only. Your money back if not 100% satisfied."

Simon and Schuster had been able to drum up advance sales of only 800 copies; an additional 1,000 copies were given on consignment to the American News Company. That left the publishers with an additional 1,800 copies to sell; surely it wouldn't be that difficult. To spur interest they gave out free copies of the book at the American Booksellers' Association convention in New York City and ran a second ad on March 23 announcing that the $1.35 book, complete with pencil, eraser, and solution book, was "ready at last!"

Although F.P.A. had refused to write a foreword for the book, he contributed his help with a mini book review in his "Conning Tower" column on publication day:

> Hooray! Hooray! Hooray! Hooray!
> *The Cross Word Puzzle Book*'s out today.

To everyone's surprise, the 3,600 copies sold out immediately. By the end of the year, through reprints and two new series, a total of 350,000 crossword books had been sold with 150,000 books being plucked off the shelves on one December day alone. The crossword craze had begun!

Crosswords provided the grist for reporters' mills with every item of crossword trivia being chronicled by the media. These were some of the tidbits that appeared in various newspapers between 1924 and 1925:

- Three hundred people gathered in New York City on May 18, 1924, to form the Crossword Puzzlers' Association of America. The group resolved to use dictionary words only and to limit or abolish unfamiliar, foreign, archaic, technical, and obsolete words in crosswords.
- Hundreds of people flocked to the Bronx Zoo to honor the emu, gnu, and boa, who "play such important roles in the country's fourth greatest industry."
- Professor Warner Fite, head of Princeton University's department of philosophy, offered a prize to the student who could construct a crossword having two complete and different solutions.
- Reverend George F. McElvein of Pittsburgh set up a large crossword on a blackboard and distributed printed copies of the definitions to his worshipers. The puzzle, containing words from Proverbs 1 and 10, was completed in fifteen minutes and was then used as the theme for the sermon.
- Welz Nathan was fined $5.00 and remanded to jail for an evening for obstructing traffic in a restaurant. He and three friends were so involved in solving a crossword that they refused to leave when the owner tried to close the establishment. Nathan opted to finish the puzzle in a four-letter place of confinement.
- Dean F. Paul Anderson, head of the electrical engineering department at the University of Kentucky, established a course in crosswords.

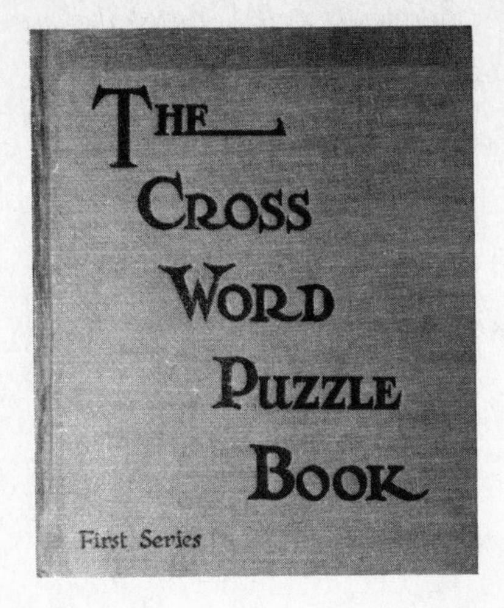

Cover of *The Cross Word Puzzle Book*, which was published on April 10, 1924

The crossword grid even appeared on clothing.

- Fannie Goldner, a 103-year-old nursing-home resident, was an avid crossword enthusiast who thought the puzzles weren't "hard enough."
- The Legal Aid organization in Cleveland received an average of ten letters a day from wives whose husbands ignored them because of their obsession with crosswords. Wives wrote that their husbands "will either have to spend some time with their families" or they "will obtain divorces."
- Theodore Koerner of Brooklyn asked his wife for help in solving a crossword. She begged off, claiming exhaustion. Koerner shot her (superficially) and then shot himself (fatally).
- The Pennsylvania Railroad placed three sets of reference books on its trains for passengers who needed assistance in solving puzzles.
- Two sisters, Isabel and Jennie McKoy of Lewisbury, New Jersey, announced their double engagement through a crossword.
- Purchasers of dresses sporting a crossword motif received a book of puzzles as a bonus from the manufacturer. To qualify for future discounts on his clothing, they had to return the book with all the puzzles solved correctly.
- The president of an athletic union contended that crosswords interfered with the training of "football players, sprinters and other young men engaged in like activities of paramount importance." He feared that the "athletic supremacy of the United States" was being threatened by the crossword and urged its abolition.
- Mrs. Mara Zaba of Chicago, complaining that she was a "cross-word widow," sued her husband for nonsupport. Mr. Zaba was so engrossed in solving crosswords that he didn't have enough time to work. Judge Sabath ordered Zaba to limit himself to three puzzles a day and devote the rest of his time to domestic duties.

Reporters weren't the only ones taken up by crossworditis. Cartoonists had a field day satirizing the country's obsession with the crossword. But it was the producers of mah-jongg sets who felt the greatest impact of the craze—their sales plummeted drastically when the world switched its attention to crosswords. Overnight, mah-jongg players were labeled out-of-date. And the winning entrant in the old *Life* magazine's "Name a Crossword Scene" contest won $500.00 for this caption: "The game that separated Pa from Ma Jong."

Ads for crossword parties appeared in magazines and newspapers. Packets comprising several copies of the same puzzle printed on heavy boards were sold—thus allowing many people to work concurrently on the same puzzle. Parties became much less social as guests competed ruthlessly against each other for the fastest solution to a crossword.

Subsidiary industries were also affected by the craze. Dictionary and thesaurus sales increased dramatically. Pocket dictionaries became fashionable, and there were even wrist dictionaries, worn instead of watches. Crossword jewelry, ranging in price from 50 cents to $35.00 was offered for sale.

Even show business wasn't immune. *Puzzles of 1925,* an Elsie Janis Broadway revue, satirized the fad with a scene set in a sanatorium for crossword-puzzle fans—the attending physician tried to "cure" patients who had gone mad trying to solve crosswords.

The crossword editors at the *World* hardly had time to relish all this hoopla: Frantically editing weekly puzzles, they also had to produce two new books in 1924. Farrar recalled her most vivid memory of this period in an interview she gave in 1982: "We used to get in a barouche and drive up and down Fifth Avenue. One of us would run into a bookstore and ask how many puzzle books had been sold that day, and the answer would be in the thousands. We were young and very excited."

Like all fads, the crossword craze tapered off, of course, but it left millions of fans loyally devoted to the crossword as a regular form of entertainment. Each subsequent generation has produced new crossword devotees and new crossword constructors.

Margaret Petherbridge, who left the *World* to marry publisher John Farrar in 1926, was the person most instrumental in the evolution of crosswords from the emu-moa-roc variety to the sophisticated form of wordplay prevalent today.

As editor of the Simon & Schuster series for sixty years, a feat unparalleled in publishing history, and as puzzle editor of *The New York Times* for twenty-seven years, Margaret Farrar was lovingly revered as the "belle dame" of crosswords. Although she always referred to her life's work as a "completely accidental

It was no longer chic to play mah-jongg during the crossword craze of 1924–25.

There were 138,250 people entered in *Life* magazine's "Name a Crossword Scene" contest in 1924. The first-prize winner earned $500 for this caption—"The game that separated Pa from Ma Jong."

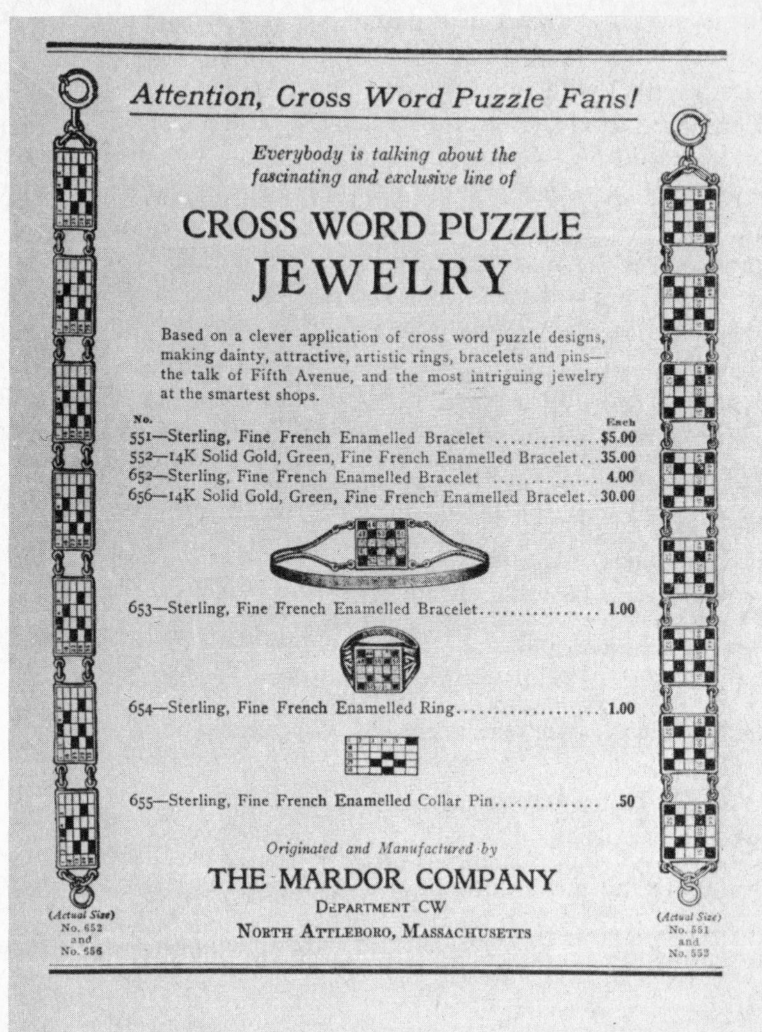

The crossword grid appeared on bracelets, rings, and collar pins.

career," her standards of excellence, easy rapport with constructors, methodical editing, and absolute fairness molded the crossword into the complex brainteaser it is today.

The New York Times, for many years the only newspaper without a crossword, quietly introduced its Sunday puzzle page in February 1942 with this brief announcement:

"Beginning today, *The New York Times* inaugurates a puzzle page. There will be two puzzles each Sunday—one with a flavor of current events and general information, and one varied in theme, ranging from puzzles in a lighter vein, like today's smaller one, to diagramless puzzles of a general nature."

The apocryphal story is that Arthur Sulzberger, publisher of the *Times,* decided to include a puzzle after he found himself buying *The New York Herald Tribune* for its crossword.

Its new puzzle editor was, of course, the redoubtable Margaret Farrar. Her instructions to use news-oriented clues were evident in the first *Times* crossword:

Black Sea naval base	Odessa
Reluctant allies of Germany	Finns
Nazi submarine base in Belgium	Ostend

For the "lighter puzzle," Farrar chose "Riddle Me This," a forerunner of Puns and Anagrams, and used peppier clues:

Where the waves are permanent	Strands
Behaved like a bird	Larked
He goes overboard frequently	Diver
Bring on the vittles	Cater

Gradually the news content was dropped, as were dull definitions.

In the beginning, words were clued in cut-and-dried dictionary terms.

Pertaining to kidneys	Renal
Possessor	Owner
Spit	Expectorate

Farrar, pioneering the use of creative cluing, encouraged constructors to look for "fresh and felicitious" ways to define words. Examples of her editorial work show how she thought of new angles for familiar words:

Answer Word	Constructor	Farrar
And so	——to bed	Part of et cetera
Also	——ran	What is more
Slowest	Pokiest	Poky, plus
Waste	"——not, want . . ."	Nuclear problem

Eventually, her constructors responded with creations of their own:

Baby's second word?	Dada
Something for the record	Album
Stowe way	Ski trail
Dotty inventor?	Morse
"Pain in the neck," in a way	Drip
Supporters of virgin wool	Ewes
Material material	Loom
After this, get cross	Criss
Party crumbs?	Cads

Farrar credits advertising pro Harold T. Bers with developing the thematic puzzle—his "Catalogue" crossword, for instance, with its related definitions of catbird seat, catacombs, Kitty Hawk, and pussyfoot.

Other constructors followed suit and now themed puzzles dominate Sunday newspapers and crossword books. Clever constructors have been able to take ordinary subjects, clue them cleverly, and amuse solvers. Examples include Maura Jacobson's "Names Game":

Paddled	Rhoda bout
Sudden breeze	Gustave wind
Of negligible worth	Noah count
Tolstoy epic	Warren peace

Merryl Maleska's "Going Places":

Car wash for a bike?	Rinse cycle
Riding the railroad?	In training
Piano mover?	Van Cliburn
Tumbrel turns?	Cartwheels

and William Lutwiniak's "Meaningful Duos":

Totie-Franchot	Fieldstone
Lucille-Bert	Ball parks
Abzug-Reed	Bella donna
Grant-George Washington	Woodcarver

When the *Times* started a daily crossword, Farrar's workload increased accordingly, but the puzzles remained of the same high caliber.

Farrar, who worked from her Manhattan apartment, managed to raise two daughters and a son. Almost of necessity, she became a night owl, starting her day late in the afternoon and working into the wee hours. She found that the editorial work flowed faster in the silence of the night. She never tried to rise early, and only those who didn't know her dared to call her before noon.

Farrar's mandatory retirement from the *Times* in 1969 generated a flood of letters, some of which appeared in the magazine section of January 26. Don Parks penned a memorable farewell in verse:

Hail Margaret (Gretchen, Maggie, Meg)!
Thou wast, or wert, a good old egg!
The ani in the upas tree,
The ern upon the Azov Sea,
Sing ave and adieu to thee!
The tribes of Otoe and of Ute you
So frequently described salute you!
You will be missed in Etna, Tara,
St. Lo, Samoa, Omsk and Nara!
What will you do when you retire?
Raise eland? Or become an ayah?
Or maybe read a book or two—
Emma? Kipling's Kim? Omoo?

"Retirement" didn't seem to be a word that Farrar could define—she was busier than ever after 1969. She continued editing the Simon & Schuster series and calendars, the *Los Angeles Times* Syndicate puzzles and the Pocket Books crossword series. "I keep trying to retire," she once said, "but I just can't seem to stop."

In fact, Farrar took on another career—as an awarder of prizes at crossword competitions. Here she had an opportunity to meet solvers, constructors, and other kindred spirits. Her annual trip

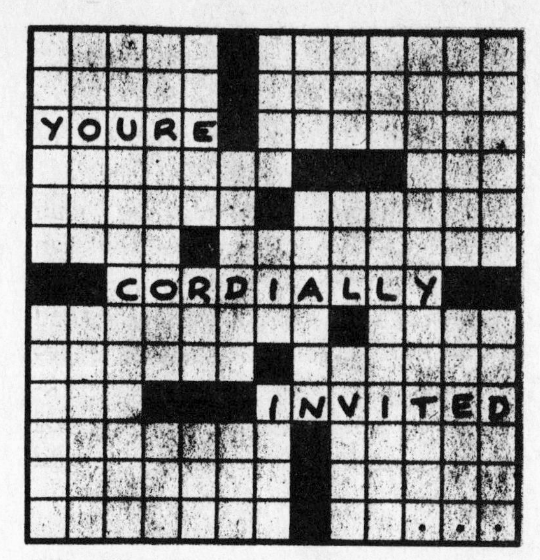

The invitation to the party for Margaret Farrar celebrating her sixty-year editorship of the Simon & Schuster series

Margaret Farrar—the person most responsible for the popularization of the crossword

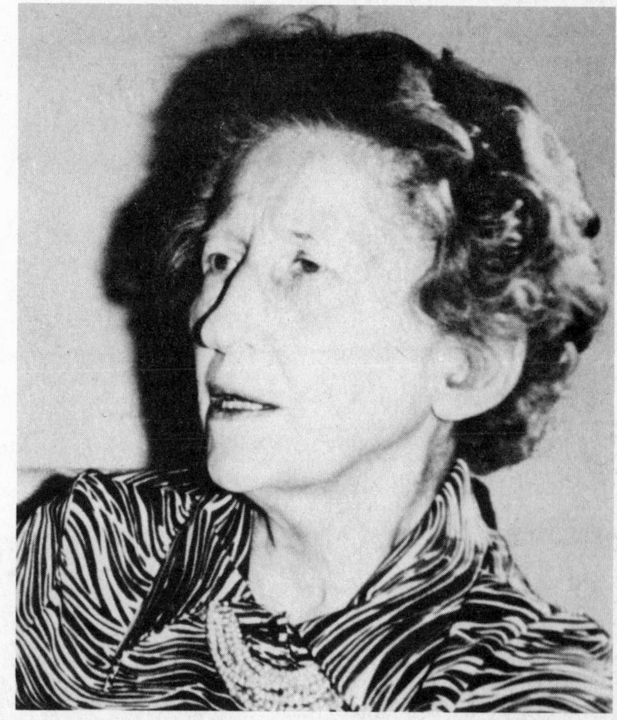

to the Stamford Marriott Crossword Competition was perhaps the only thing that ever got her out of bed before noon. Grimacing visibly when told she had to be ready to leave her apartment at nine in the morning, she muttered something about "the crack of dawn," but nothing would keep her from attending.

Farrar's passion for crosswords never diminished. Although she slowed down physically as she aged, her mental agility was never affected. When she was told at eighty-one that she might not want to be driven to Stamford in a sports car, she humphed with a chuckle and said, "I know how to get into a sports car—fanny first!"

The sixtieth anniversary of the Simon & Schuster crosswords series was celebrated in 1984 with two back-to-back events. On April 8, Margaret Farrar presided over the first-ever gathering of crossword editors. The wit and warmth that had endeared her to her colleagues over the years came through when, after blowing out the candles on her crossword cake, she commented that her job had always been "a piece of cake." The next evening Farrar hosted a "Now We Are Sixty" party at a private club in New York City. It was her last public appearance before her death on June 11, 1984.

Farrar left a legacy in the many crossword constructors and editors who were her disciples. Her commitment to style, quality, and innovation continue in their work. Thanks to her brilliance in an "accidental career," crosswords are an entertaining part of over fifty million lives.

RONNIE ALLEN

A ONE-TIME elementary school teacher and principal, Ronnie Allen was involved in California's education world for more than fifteen years. She has a bachelor's degree in history/French from Stanford University and a master's degree in educational administration from the California State University at Sacramento. But in 1982, divorced and with her own children gone from the nest, she moved to the San Francisco Bay Area and changed careers. "I gave myself six months to sell a puzzle—if I didn't I told myself I'd have to look for other work. Two days before my time limit was up, I sold my first crossword. I was thrilled!" she recalls. The first acceptance was enough of an impetus for her to stick to her plan.

One of the persons who most influenced her was Mike Shenk, of *Games* (see page 186). He rejected her 15×15 crossword with a San Francisco theme, but told her how to improve on it and gave her the names of other publishers to contact. That first puzzle was "so awful," she remembers now, that she threw it away. But by following Shenk's advice, she soon began placing her puzzles with various editors.

It's difficult to break into the puzzle world, she explains, because so many editors just don't have the time to work with new constructors. Instead, they rely on their own detailed "guidelines" to help the would-be constructor along. Allen says that "of all the publications I submitted to, successfully or not, only one offered me any helpful criticism." Puzzle constructing is pretty much a do-it-yourself and learn-as-you-go process. There are only a few books about crossword construction—*A Pleasure in Words,* by Eugene T. Maleska, and *The Compleat Cruciverbalist,* by Mel Rosen and Stan Kurzban, are both good ones.

By studying each publisher's guidelines, Allen was able to work her entries up from amateurish to professional. She now constructs puzzles for many publications—Penny Press magazines, Will Weng's *Crosswords Club,* the Running Press series, *Games,* the *L.A. Times* Syndicate and the *New York Times* books. When she's "into it" she constructs a puzzle a day; when she's "busy elsewhere," it's one a week. Working from her home in Santa Cruz, California, she uses a variety of reference books.

Some editors, Allen has found, like new-wave clues, brand names, and punny themes. Other are happy to keep crosswords on a more even keel with straightforward definitions and clues. Since Allen creates puzzles for a wide variety of publications, she changes styles as her mood dictates. "I have to deal with different editors in different ways," she says.

Although Allen now lists her occupation as "cruciverbalist," her other income is earned from her position as editor of the Stanford alumni magazine, a quarterly publication, which includes a puzzle page. Most of the puzzles thereon are her crosswords, though after sending out requests for submissions, she has included Double-Crostics, fillers, and variety puzzles as well. A group of Allen's friends test-solve the alumni puzzles she constructs. The proud owner of a new photocopy machine, she runs off copies to distribute to the group, which returns completed puzzles with feedback about clues and definitions.

Allen's interest in puzzles goes back as far as childhood when "I'd try to solve anything I could find. My mother was a puzzle fanatic too. Once during a newspaper strike we made up our own puzzles and sent them to each other to make up for the ones we missed in the papers." Her sons (now twenty-five and twenty-six) don't solve crosswords, nor does her second husband. However, he "does pat me on the back a lot when he sees my name in print."

All puzzles, of course, embody the twin elements of disguise (on the constructor's part) and discovery (by the solver). Allen's gimmicky puzzles reflect her ability to camouflage clues in an offbeat way. The puzzle title and/or blurb gives some indication of the trick contained within. In three of Allen's most memorable crosswords she used "&" for "and," "8" for "ate," and "woman" or "women" for "man" or "men."

From "First R8":

Tardy person's excuse	Better l8 than never
F. Scott Fitzgerald title	The Gr8 Gatsby
Assists the prosecution	Turns st8s evidence
Laugh In award	Fickle Finger of F8

Very valuable	Worth its w8 in gold
Live dangerously	Sk8 on thin ice

From "St&ard Time":

Halftime entertainment	Marching b&
Indispensable assistant	Right h& man
European capital	London Engl&
Indian leader	Mahatma G&hi

From "Womenagerie, speaking out for equal rights":

Cherchez la femme, to Holmes	Elewomentary
Ladies' lethe	Womental block
The economics of feminism	Supply and dewomand
"Go west, young girl"	Womanifest destiny
Ms. editors	Womanagement

She also likes alliterative clues:

Mediocre mark	Cee
Herded herds	Drove
Stag's splendor	Antler
Hammer heel	Peen
Maa ma	Ewe

and unusual definitions:

He's a rough character	Mauler
Om and om and om	Mantra
Anchorman of yore	Crier
Shade of blue	True
Poe-tic inspiration	Raven

Allen also constructs puzzles with definitions that reveal the themed clues obliquely. In a "Basketball" puzzle the clues had nothing to do with the sport, but the answers yielded basketball terms:

Judicial call for quiet	Order in the court
Washday container	Laundry basket
Prosecutor's adversary	Defense attorney
One's own seraph	Guardian angel

In "Order Blanks," themed entries related to numerical order—"fifth column," "second wind," "sixth sense."

Ronnie Allen is firmly in favor of the loosening up of crossword-puzzle rules—going beyond *Webster's* definitions into original and imaginative constructions. Actually, she says, crosswords are accessible to more people when constructors "use our wits more, our dictionaries less."

(see next page for the puzzle)

CINEMA SUBTRACTION by Ronnie Allen

(SEE PAGE 262 FOR SOLUTION)

ACROSS

1 Etc. category
5 Bedouins and Syrians
10 South American plain
15 Dextrous and valent prefix
19 "—— girl!"
20 *Orphée* painter
21 Plume source
22 Engendered
23 Jet Set original
24 Jewelry lock
25 —— evil (act the monkey)
26 Advantage
27 With *The,* Julie Harris is hot stuff in the bridal party
31 Cold cube in Köln
32 Incontrovertible
33 Make lace
34 Conspicuous
36 Upped the ante
39 —— of luxury
42 British House denizen
43 Stage direction
44 Goldbrick
45 *Fleur-de-* ——
48 Haste by-product
51 Serpentine saying
52 Encounters
53 Ghastly
55 Minced oath
56 MD's org.
57 Latin rhythm
58 Ceres, to the Greeks
60 Like the hills
61 One in the fast lane?
63 Map within a map
65 In a ferocious manner
67 Providing for the squeaky wheel
69 Rock group, for short
70 Valuable finds
71 Forgives
73 High IQ society
75 Waver
78 Black-white connection
79 Righteous Greek goddess
81 Beautify
83 Harem chamber
84 Dance component
86 Fishing spinners
87 Clotho, Lachesis and Atropos
88 It's "up the river"
89 Seoul-ful country
91 GI address
92 "Monopoly" purchase
93 —— *in the Head*
94 Roosevelt pet
96 Safari helper
98 Symbol of spring
99 Temporary immigrant
102 Curve segment
103 Receipts
104 Indisposed
105 Joanne Woodward's split personality at poker
113 Venus de ——
115 Emulate Sinatra
116 What "Who" is on
117 ". . . going to St. ——"
118 Roman poet
119 Came up
120 Join forces
121 Wrongful act
122 Requisite
123 Adam minus the fig leaf
124 Serviced the sedan
125 Bristle

DOWN

1 Part of MCP
2 Bookkeeping entry
3 Attempt
4 Strokes
5 Agreement
6 Pocahontas' husband
7 "I smell ——"
8 Piffle
9 Roman Basilica
10 Coin of Castile
11 Prepared wine or cheese
12 TV's talking horse
13 "The —— mightier than the sword."
14 Musically directionless
15 Honest Pres.
16 Cooper's common man has car trouble
17 Meir successor
18 I.e., i.e.
28 One with regrets
29 Cock's domain
30 Aura
35 Dies ——
36 P.T. activity
37 Spirit, in España
38 Second chance for Jimmy Stewart to prevaricate
39 Criminal plumbing problem for Bogey
40 Discover
41 Professor of "Clue"
44 Relig. school
46 Drew Barrymore sees red
47 Ravi Shankar's instrument
49 First of Mae West's trio
50 MacDonald's co-star
52 Coleridge character
53 Insinuate
54 Gives attention to
57 Casaba or honeydew
58 Takes out of print

59 Quoted by Poe
62 Pot top
64 Big rigs
66 Right, by golly
68 Home of mythical lion
71 Barrel
72 Preposition
74 Flooding
76 Ancient bureaucrat
77 More like a day in June
80 Unkempt one
82 Electric swimmer
85 Bosc or Anjou
87 Assertive
88 ". . . ——, wear it!"
90 Dismounted
92 Tortoise competitor
93 "Sweet Adeline" range
95 Depth charge
97 Brought home the bacon
98 Went on a hunger strike
99 Shakespeare's Athenian
100 Drab in the Army
101 Firma or cotta
103 Beau ——
106 Appropriated
107 Irrigation device
108 Aboriginal Japanese
109 Cheat sheet
110 Bacchanal cry
111 TV adjustment
112 *¿Como* ——?
114 Eccentric

EMILY COX AND HENRY RATHVON

CHARMING AND ATTRACTIVE, Emily Cox and Henry Rathvon are a youthful duo who have mastered the art of cryptic construction. They have a loyal following but are intensely private people who keep a low profile so that "an air of mystery" will "cloak not only cryptic crosswords, but their makers as well."

Once the editors of *Four-Star Puzzler,* they now construct the monthly cryptic crossword for *The Atlantic,* act as contributing editors to *Games,* and alternate constructing *The Boston Globe* Sunday crossword with Henry Hook. They work from their home in Hershey, Pennsylvania, where, they confess, "the air is redolent of cooking chocolate."

Aficionados of cryptic crosswords delight in the varied forms of wordplay that distinguish this type of puzzle from traditional ones. For the uninitiated, clues in cryptic crosswords consist of two parts—a literal definition of the answer and a subsidiary clue involving wordplay. The first step in solving cryptics is to distinguish between the two parts by mentally repunctuating the clue. The second step is to discover the type of wordplay involved.

Cox and Rathvon give their solvers a square deal by creating clues that are fair, literate, and terse. Examples of definitions from the Cox/Rathvon file show how each word leads directly to the answer.

Double definitions are merely two definitions of the same word side by side:

Flatten vegetable	Squash
Tire Reagan's Vice President	Bush
Secure place to keep horses	Stable
Here is a gift	Present
Current conscription	Draft

In anagram clues the letters of one word are rearranged to form a new word:

Elf upset priest	Sprite
Drug is ruinous to a pie	Opiate

Armed citizens routed evil giants	Vigilantes
Lost abstract art, say	Astray
Count rats—lousy rats	Turncoats

Homophone clues use words that sound like something else:

Audibly elevate beams	Rays
Reportedly know a man who sailed an ark	Noah
King's chair is tossed audibly	Throne
Say, 120 minutes or more belonging to us	Ours
Sounds like whaler is one moaning	Wailer

Deletions involve subtracting parts of words to form new words:

Lowly laborer cut end off flower	Peon~~y~~
Actor Hoffman has not finished cleaning	Dustin~~g~~
Experts not finished writing	Pros~~e~~
Headless guards in doorways	~~S~~entries

Containers break a word down into its components, which are inside and outside of each other:

Lear is holding the shoe material	Lea(the)r
Murder in place with frying pan	S(kill)et
She keeps warm wrap	S(heat)he
Kept Communist outside of state	Re(Maine)d
Jazzman shows warmth about personal computer	He(PC)at
Snarl during feline conversation	C(hitch)at

Hidden words are buried inside the clue:

Meal amid pure pasta	puRE PASTa
In Sparta, the nature goddess	SpartA THE NAture
Get a book partially outlawed	geT A BOOk
Secretariat artfully carries lasso	SecretaRIAT Artfully

Charades break words into two or more consecutive parts, which are individually clued:

Look—Ms. Derek in a pavilion	Gaze + Bo
Dad's wise selection from a text	Pas + sage
Ponders 1,000 exercises	M + uses
Excuse to share beer	Ration + ale

In reversals the answers spell something else backward:

Returning students make a mistake	Slip up
God of love is angry, uprising	Eros
For sport lash back	Golf

The puzzles Cox and Rathvon construct for *The Atlantic* are doubly devious for they usually require a two-part solving process. In their "Sixism" puzzle, solvers had first to define a cryptic clue and then shorten or lengthen it before placing it in the diagram. Half the clues led to five-letter words and half to seven-letter words. However, "in the interest of equality" all answers had to be six letters long before being placed in the grid. Examples show the clue, correct answer, wordplay involved, and the word that went into the diagram:

Planet with hot, wet land	Marsh—charade—Marsha
Current passenger is more bitter	Acrider—charade—Acider
Don't start broadcasts for so long	Adios—deletion—Audios
One German passion	Anger—charade—Danger

In an "Upstairs Downstairs" puzzle the grid was divided into two identical upper and lower levels and answers were clued in pairs. Solvers first answered each set of clues and then placed them into two symmetrically identical spots in the grid. As a bonus (and as a solving hint) the correct solution yielded an appropriate phrase ("double decker") running down the center of the diagram. Examples of the clued sets include:

Hearing is associated with sensor (Nose); Heartlessly cut prophet (Seer)

Southern soldiers concerned with bees (Rebs); Luxuriantly growing row (rank)

Cox and Rathvon were even trickier with a "Go-Betweens" puzzle that required multiple solving steps. The first stage was to answer each Across clue with two words of the same length that differed from each other by only two letters. Next, you had to determine a third word, or "go-between," which differed from each of the two answers by just a single letter—and place that word in the diagram. Examples:

Different voice = Other-Utter = Otter
Kids feelings = Teases-Senses = Tenses
Traps wasps = Corners-Hornets = Cornets

Cox and Rathvon drew upon an old form of wordplay, spoonerisms, for a puzzle by the same name. A spoonerism is a transposition of two consonant sounds in a word or phrase to create a new word, e.g., "butterfly," "flutter by." Spoonerisms are named for William Archibald Spooner (1844–1930), a nervous clergyman-educator, whose proclivity for accidentally transposing phrases into humorous expressions led to coinage of the word.

In Cox/Rathvon's version, solvers had to spoonerize the answers to cryptic clues before putting them in the grid. Thus, "Some nature lovers scattered rich bedstraw" was answered by "bird watchers"; but "word botchers" was the phrase entered into the grid. Similarly, "Meal course has Dad keeping energy very high" translated to "pea soup" which was spoonerized to "sea poop."

The Enigma, the monthly magazine published by the National Puzzlers' League, frequently features spoonerisms. In the following examples, substitute a phrase for ONE, TWO, or DONE in the verse. Numerals merely indicate word lengths in each answer phrase (answers are on page 43):

The inmates played a ONE all day
But stopped each time the TWO that way.
(4,4; 5,4)

I eyed the knave, and then my hand,
To ONE and make the slam I planned.
But just as I drew out my card,
I felt us TWO, go lurching hard—
Commuters, tickets, cards, and all
In discombobulated sprawl.
(5,3,4; 4,3,5)

On Sunday morn
The church bells ONE,
The petty thieves
Prepare to DONE.
(4,4,3,7; 5,4,3,6)

The growth in popularity of cryptic crosswords was spearheaded by Will Shortz (see page 200) through *Games* magazine. He featured a warm-up cryptic in early issues and took new solvers step by step through the intricate deciphering process. Today cryptics are an integral feature of his Pencilwise section.

Shortz, always seeking new twists for his tournaments, included a separate cryptic contest during the 1983 Stamford event. More than one hundred solvers entered in two divisions—beginner and intermediate/advanced. To absolutely no one's surprise, computer analyst Philip Cohen easily won the advanced division by answering clues like these (answers are on page 43):

Perverts sound contented, back in beds (8)
Beautiful young woman's New York pace (5)
Listen, between Kenneth and Theodore, starting off smart is cowardly (14)
Mentioned clock moving back to the front after the war (9)
One at a time, with love (8)
Mount St. Helens' second eruption starting down (5)

Cohen, who received an Atari VCS 2600 for his efforts, is one of the NPL's best solvers and most active members. He is also the top cryptic-crossword solver in the United States for his knowledge of words is unequaled anywhere.

Although he usually eschews traditional crosswords, Cohen won the 1981 Stamford contest. Part of the reason for his triumph was that the playoff puzzle seemed to "be made just for me." In his words, "Two of the answers were HOUYHNHNMS ('Horses in *Gulliver's Travels*') and MR MXYZPTLK ('Superman's foe from the fifth dimension'). They were intended as stumpers, but they're just the sort of esoterica I'm good at, so I filled them in with hardly any crossing letters." Constructor Henry Hook (see page 59) was "rather chagrined" at Cohen's speedy solving and sent him a 19 × 19 congratulatory crossword afterward with this clue—"What the Marriott tourney goes to show." Cohen easily filled in the answer—"You can't HOUYHNHNM all."

Hook frequently constructs puzzles for friends. Just a few hours after the 1979 Marriott contest ended, Hook constructed a 25 × 25 crossword that included the names of all the judges who had participated that weekend. Who but Hook could have fit Doug and

Sixth Annual
Stamford Marriott
CROSSWORD PUZZLE INVITATIONAL
MARCH 4-6, 1983
Sponsored by Games Magazine and the Stamford Marriott Hotel
Coordinated by Will Shortz, Senior Editor, Games
INCLUDING—NEW THIS YEAR—AMERICA'S FIRST
CRYPTIC CROSSWORD TOURNAMENT!

Friday, March 4, 1983

7:00-10:00 PM The Stamford Marriott's First Cryptic Crossword Competition. The contest will consist of four standard 15 × 15 block-style cryptic puzzles of easy to moderate difficulty, created and edited especially for this contest. Solvers may compete in either a "Beginner" or "Intermediate / Advanced" classification, and will have 30 minutes in which to work each puzzle. Special guests will discuss cryptic crosswords and answer questions about cryptics before the rounds actually begin. The contest is free to all contestants who compete in the American-style tournament Saturday and Sunday. For a $10 registration fee, a solver may compete in the cryptic tournament only. It will be an experience!

10:00-11:00 PM Wine and cheese reception. Sit back and relax after the evening's cogitation.

Saturday, March 5, 1983

9:00-11:00 AM Registration for the American Crossword Competition
11:00-12:30 PM Morning Rounds—three puzzles
12:30- 1:30 PM Light Lunch (optional)
2:30- 4:00 PM Afternoon Rounds—three puzzles
8:00-10:00 PM An evening of non-competition word games and puzzles. Relax and enjoy the fun. The games will include a novel "Crossword Relay"—the world's first such relay to the best of our knowledge—and "Trivia Baseball," in which it helps to know a lot of useless facts about a lot of useless things. Plus other entertainment.

Sunday, March 6, 1983

8:30 AM Standings posted
9:00-10:00 AM Final Round—one puzzle
11:00-11:30 AM Championship Playoff—in which the three top contestants will compete on a sudden-death playoff puzzle printed behind large plexiglass boards
1:00- 2:30 PM Awards Banquet. The prizes will be presented by Margaret Farrar, editor and co-editor of the original Simon and Schuster crossword series since 1924.

The highlight of the 1983 Stamford Marriott Tournament was a cryptic crossword contest. Prior to the contest, Henry Rathvon discussed cryptic cluing.

Philip Cohen, winner of the 1981 Stamford Marriott Tournament

Jan Heller (see page 54), William F. Shortz (see page 200), Margaret Farrar (see page 24), Threba Johnson, Stephanie Spadaccini, Norton Rhoades, Maura Jacobson (see page 76), Jordan Lasher (see page 88), and Helene Hovanec (your author) into one puzzle?

Cohen's trademark is voluminous letter writing, each letter composed on his personal computer, photocopied, and mailed to dozens of pen pals. After the 1983 NPL centennial convention Cohen composed an eighteen-page single-spaced recount of the weekend and sent it to numerous friends.

Since Cox and Rathvon don't travel the puzzle circuit it's difficult for solvers to let them know how highly regarded they are. One indication of the impact they've made on followers of their *Atlantic* cryptics showed up in the numerous letters to the editors printed in that magazine for a period of several months.

Ronald Arledge opened a Pandora's box when he wrote that he had "solved every cryptic crossword puzzle" in *The Atlantic* and wondered if "any other reader" could "make this claim."

Joseph T. D'Ulisse, dubbing himself the "world's greatest puzzler," claimed that he had not only solved all the puzzles, but had done them "in ink!"

Kurt A. Young cited his achievements: "I have solved all the puzzles. I read once through the clues and then type the solutions while blindfolded."

"Up until a year ago," wrote Paul J. Nahin, "I regularly solved each month's Puzzler without bothering to look at the clues. And since September of 1984 I have been solving each one before it appears in print."

Stevan Northcutt went one step further by admitting that his "miniature schnauzer, Zonker, spends hours working on the Puzzler. He can't hold a pen, of course, so he yips and yowls the answers to me in Morse code, and I write them down."

Gregoire Turgeon added a new dimension—money—for he solved the puzzles and then sold "the red-hot answers to an appreciative clientele, mostly university professors and United States congressmen." Although he wasn't sure why they wanted the answers, they paid "well."

Well, cryptic fans need not fear that the Cox/Rathvon creative well will ever run dry, for while puzzledom's most creative couple guards its privacy, they're busy turning out a wealth of excellent material for an appreciative public.

ANSWERS—COX/RATHVON

Spoonerisms

1. Card game—guard came
2. Trump the jack—jump the track
3. Peal from the steeple—steal from the people

Cryptic Clues

1. Co(rrup)ts—Reversal/container
2. N.Y. + mph—Charade
3. Chic + Ken(hear)Ted—Charade/container
4. Peacetime—Homophone of timepiece with each syllable switched
5. A + t (time) + tender—Charade
6. St. + e (Helens' second) + e (eruption) + d (start of down)—Charade

CRYPTIC CROSSWORD by Emily Cox and Henry Rathvon

(SEE PAGE 262 FOR SOLUTION)

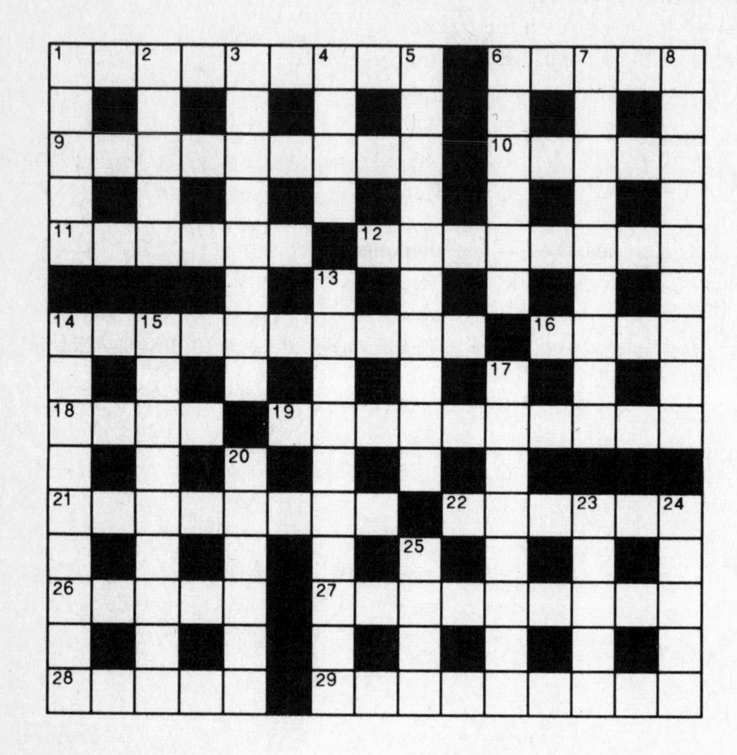

ACROSS

1 State nominates liberal (9)
6 Just so absorbing to Zeno's disciple (5)
9 The pig sat smeared with food (9)
10 Carefully move left and stand (5)
11 Quit the last course audited (6)
12 Preacher bloke reclined (8)
14 Poems about a poor French palace (9)
16 Look desirously at meat of frog legs (4)
18 Great monkey's stare (4)
19 Beginners in anti-Soviet rioting (10)
21 Inspired article in *Money* (8)
22 Endlessly talk about Olympic event (6)
26 French city harbors English kin (5)
27 Learn of and teach all about sorrow (9)
28 Exercise place is back (3-2)
29 Check with coach during inactivity (9)

DOWN

1 Mohegan's chief employed thought (5)
2 Approaches snare carelessly (5)
3 Alien and the boy: quite spacy (8)
4 Farm animals head off for grain (4)
5 Figuring course, I chart time incorrectly (10)
6 Inattentive general nabbed by agent (6)
7 Attack Laughton's plays (9)
8 Company columnist is straining things (9)
13 Completely change covering he got smashed (10)
14 Hoboes making Virginia-Georgia connections (9)
15 Congressman has to dislike show (9)
17 Nun keeping in dark (8)
20 Actress Peters gets upset (6)
23 Perform amid 101 plants (5)
24 Small part of a dollar for perfume (5)
25 Fish with string (4)

FRANCES HANSEN

FRANCES HANSEN, a slim, lovely lady from New Jersey, is a former Sunday-school teacher who does all she can to deceive you. When she's not concocting the five-line limericks that are her trademark, she's dreaming up ways to make the solving process just a little bit trickier for unsuspecting puzzlers.

Her "Scrambling Around" puzzle (published in the *Times* on Easter Sunday, 1977) required solvers to replace the letters EGG with a drawing of an egg; trusting solvers couldn't figure out how the answer to "Actress Samantha," which should be "Eggar," could take up only three squares. Other eggs-acting clues included:

Variety headline, 1929	Wall Street lays an ⬭
What does an Easter bunny do?	Puts all his ⬭s in one basket
Is an intellectual artistic?	Can an ⬭head grow an Easter ⬭

This puzzle so enraged one solver that she complained bitterly to editor Eugene Maleska: "I have been a crossword puzzle fan for almost 50 years. But what has happened to the once great Sunday *New York Times* puzzles distresses me. The 'gimmicks' are ridiculous and today's is the worst. How about going back to good, regular, challenging, intelligent puzzles?"

This was definitely a minority opinion for other solvers sent Maleska their completed puzzles with all the eggs drawn neatly in place; one solver even colored in every egg! Margaret Farrar took time out to congratulate Hansen with this postcard: "I'm still missing a few eggs, but so far there is none on your face. Cheers and showers of April greetings."

In "Paging William Tell" Hansen used an → to replace the word "arrow." Clues and answers included the following:

Rosemary's Baby's mother	Mia F→
Start of an old rhyme	I shot an → into the air

Who killed Cock Robin	I said the sp→
What Molly Malone did	Wheeled her wheel b→
Barbs of "outrageous fortune"	Slings and →s
Query re your bones?	Are they h→ed to the m→

In other rebus puzzles Hansen used flags, roses, bells, stars, moons, sharps, flats, and balls in place of those words in the grid. In "Vacancies" solvers had to leave certain squares empty to represent the word "blank," e.g., "—— check" and "point ——." Hansen even included an apology to solvers in one of the clues—"forgive my ——ety —— puzzle."

Hansen's other specialties are limericks and poems. In her pre-crossword days she composed light verses for *Cosmopolitan* and *Good Housekeeping* and it seemed natural for her to draw upon this background for crosswords. The first verse she used in a crossword was simply titled "Limerick":

Said W. Somerset Maugham,
"I shall visit the island of Guam.
If I find it is hot,
I shall leave on the spot.
I detest feeling overly waugham."

When Hansen sent this puzzle to Farrar, the *Times* editor was reluctant to use it for two reasons—she had never done anything like it before and she couldn't believe the verse was a Hansen original. Hansen convinced Farrar of the authenticity of the verse by sending in more original poetry. Farrar then decided to use the puzzle and broke ground for yet another innovation in the crossword world.

Other Hansen verses which have found their way into crosswords include:

Fast Talk

He sighs, he says alas a lot,
His dolor is disquieting.
Is he in love or ill or what?
Relax, he's merely dieting.

With Malice Toward None

A tolerant man of Tabriz
Found several flies on his cheese;
When told he must swat,
He said, "No, I will not,
They are welcome to eat what
they please."

Marathon

I envy you the merry chase
But I'm disposed to shun it.
Though I enjoy the human race
I'd rather walk than run it.

Don't Hold Your Breath

A gullible lady of Cannes
Met a curious kind of a man
And their tale I'll relate
When I get it all straight
In a verse I am able to scan.

Always a voracious reader and avid Scrabble player, Hansen didn't start solving crosswords until she was in her forties. She used them to fill the void that developed when she quit teaching Sunday school after a twelve-year stint and found that all her friends were addicted to the Sunday *Times* puzzle. They were intent on filling in every square in the grid by early Sunday afternoon and made frequent calls to each other to check clues and answers and compare notes.

Hansen made the leap from solving to constructing because she "had this crazy idea that constructing must be easier than solving since you knew all the answers." She had a "rude awakening" when she discovered just how difficult it was to construct.

Hansen sent her first crossword, a 23 × 23, to Margaret Farrar at the *Times*. The most memorable mistake Hansen made was to put the puzzle on specially printed oversize grids. Not knowing any of the rules, she thought this would be an appropriate way to submit the puzzle. Farrar couldn't ignore Hansen's puzzle for it covered her entire desk and even spilled over onto the floor.

Rejecting the puzzle, Farrar sent Hansen a two-page sheet of rules and encouraged her to revise the puzzle and resubmit it. Hansen followed Farrar's advice and soon saw her first published puzzle, "Ykcowrebbaj," in the Sunday *Times*. The puzzle has become a classic, for it introduced solvers to a whole new way of looking at crosswords—backward! The top entry was clued as "Well-known part of 'Ykcowrebbaj' " and was answered by "ebarg tuo shtar emom eht dna."

Hansen used reverse entries in other puzzles, such as "Songs in Retrospect" in which the following appropriate song titles had to be entered backward in the grid—"Back Home in Tennessee," "Lulu's Back in Town," "Bring Back My Bonnie to Me," and "The Back Bay Polka."

Since her auspicious beginning in the *Times,* Hansen has constructed more than five hundred puzzles. Working in her home-office, which she dubs her "torture chamber," in Metuchen, New Jersey, she uses hundreds of reference books covering everything from popular songs to comic-book characters. Hansen is widowed and her children are grown, so she's able to work for hours on end.

In her early constructing days Hansen would spend months on one puzzle. (That's by no means a record, for Robert Stilgenbauer of Los Angeles worked from 1938 to 1949 constructing a mammoth crossword with more than six thousand clues, a feat that earned him a place in *The Guinness Book of World Records*. Stilgenbauer showed up at the 1985 Great Western Puzzle Tournament and brought some of his handsomely printed oversize puzzles with him.)

Hansen's output has speeded up considerably since those early days, which is just as well because her work is now so much in demand that there are always deadlines to be met. She takes her puzzles and reference books (including *Webster's Third*) with her on vacations. She has constructed puzzles on beaches, in airports, restaurants, and hotels.

Hansen feels that puzzles are "primarily for entertainment. You can pick up a little knowledge solving them, but it's painless." Solvers chuckle over clues and entries like these:

From "Sewing Basket":

Object of enormous value	Purl of great price
Cockfighting, e.g.	Crewel sport
Equivocates	Hems and haws
Hollander book, with *The*	*Happy Hooker*
Pepys' sign-off	And sew to bed
Quibble	Argue a petit point
Couldn't care less	Doesn't give a darn
Repair a relationship	Patch up a quarrel

From "Brooklynese":

Oily?	No I'm running late
Doze?	I'm fonder of these
Cheese!	It's wrong to swear

From "Follow the Leader":

Look follow-ups	After, alike, at, into, sharp
Push follow-ups	Bolt, bar, bike, button, cart
Hang follow-ups	Nail, fire, dog, gliding, out

Her nonthematic clues are equally clever:

Sign of spring	Aries
Misnomer for some transits	Rapid
Popular Western	Omelet
It has lots of substitutes	Sugar
Data processor's snack?	Byte
First to take a ribbing	Adam
She raised Cain	Eve

A Hansen crossword served as a springboard for humorist Russell Baker's classic "Crashing into Crosswordland" column of January 19, 1975. Baker, thwarted in his efforts to figure out the answer to "Dr. Dolittle's duck" ("Dab Dab") dozed off and crashed into the unique world of the black and white squares. There he encountered such familiar crossword denizens as "Ava (Miss Gardner), Evita (—— Peron), and Monk (Jazzman Thelonious) . . . who were ired (angry) about being trite (overworked)." Baker's masterpiece included more than sixty items of "crosswordese'' written in this manner. When Hansen wrote to Baker complimenting him on the column he sent her the original of the illustration that accompanied the article. Hansen framed it and gives it a prominent spot in her workroom.

Hansen's puzzles appear in *The New York Times,* Dell *Champion* magazines, the *L.A. Times* Syndicate, Will Weng's *Crosswords Club* and *Times* books, the Simon & Schuster books, *Games, The Crossworder's Own Newsletter,* and both Tap Osborn's and Stan Newman's Running Press series. She also constructs a 15 × 15 for *Vue,* the once-a-month fashion supplement in *The Village Voice.*

Hansen keeps herself in shape for constructing by solving crosswords every day (one in the morning with her coffee), watching TV, and reading numerous newspapers and magazines.

In a 1961 article in *The Nation,* David Cort wrote: ''Construction of a crossword unconsciously reveals the maker's whole mental furniture, his reserves of knowledge and insight. If he is a victim of rote ('sound of the surf') he will be inept ('absurd').''

Crossworders in agreement with Cort would have to say that the ''real'' Frances Hansen is witty, charming, intelligent, innovative, and never, ever inept.

(see next page for the puzzle)

GRIZZLY BUSINESS by Frances Hansen

(SEE PAGE 262 FOR SOLUTION)

ACROSS

1 Geometrical line
7 Spot for "one brief, shining moment"
14 Absolute ruler
20 Lapwing
21 Mobile milieu
22 Golonka or Francis
23 Start of a verse
26 Matilda or Ananias
27 Spirit of St. Louis?
28 First Danish king
29 ". . . some —— great . . ." (Shak.)
30 Occupancy
32 Before "amo" or "amite"
33 Oaf
34 81 Across, e.g.
35 Bill's partner
37 Hawk's claw
39 Noodlehead
43 More of verse
49 Corrida cries
50 ". . . —— man put asunder" (wedding words)
51 Pinky or Peggy
52 *Gianni Schicchi* soprano
53 Zilch
54 Shade of green
55 Greek letters
57 In a judicious way
58 Egg: prefix
59 "While ——, and you are you" (R. Browning)
60 Aggregate
61 Type of type
62 More of verse
70 Trevino's need
71 Dine late
72 Crown of Osiris
73 Clay today
74 Retiring
77 Do Gallup's job
78 Ghastly pale
79 Britisher's omega
80 Alamogordo's county
81 She was "frivolous" in song
82 Dispatch boat
84 Characteristic wine flavor
85 More of verse
90 Opposite of "yep"
91 Tough question
92 Brooklyn trailer
93 Comical Alley
94 Be overfond
95 —— Saud, founder of Saudi Arabia
97 Of imposing dimensions
101 Attack violently
105 North Carolina college
106 Not at home
107 Tabula —— (clean slate)
108 End of verse
112 Part of Greater London
113 U.S.S.R. inland body of water
114 Look upon
115 Greenstreet, the "Fat Man"
116 Loathes
117 Mall proliferation

DOWN

1 Wood-cutting residue
2 Miss Dinsmore
3 "George M."
4 Batting statistics
5 Bird's beak
6 The Dormouse spoke well of it
7 Give a hoot
8 High school subj.
9 Price slash
10 Lustrous black
11 ". . . a —— themselves" (Romans 2:14)
12 Leave out
13 Sunbather's reward
14 Synthetic fabrics
15 Slipped
16 Yarn irregularity
17 Foot: prefix
18 Humdinger
19 Good bird that deserves another?
24 Vanderbilt or Carter
25 Aplenty
31 Catch in the act
33 Whodunit hints
35 Kind of open sesame card
36 Italian innkeeper
38 Enviable poise
39 Teeterboard
40 Twiddling one's thumbs
41 Pell- ——
42 Send up an orison
43 Up —— (as yet)
44 Pedro's martini garnish
45 Spiral
46 Los ——, atomic research center
47 Bears seldom indulge in this
48 Certain U.N. fund
54 Miss Leigh, of *Psycho*
56 Mao's sucessor
57 Ill-fated aviator Post
59 —— March, dramatic date
61 Boa's cousin
63 Forever, poetically

64 Tristan's love
65 —— -de-sac (dead end)
66 Famed film collie
67 Stunned
68 *Ecole* attender
69 Document addendum
74 Like a well-kept lawn
75 Roman emperor, A.D. 69
76 Word for still waters
77 Bel ——, mild cheese
78 "—— We Got Fun?"
81 Renata of the Met
83 Excessive pride
84 Part of the psyche
86 "I'm sorry," e.g.
87 Gastronome —— -Savarin
88 Flutists or traffic pests
89 Gypsy gentleman
94 Irene of *The Awful Truth*
96 *Wedding Day* author Kay
97 Inelegant "What?"
98 *M*A*S*H* company clerk
99 River to the Rhone
100 St. Louis nine, familiarly
101 Overwhelms, in a way
102 "Wonderful one-hoss" buggy
103 Hawked
104 A —— Alfa
105 Emerald Isle
106 S. American wood sorrels
109 Wee bit
110 Bridge reversal
111 Kind of blanket

DOUG AND JANIS HELLER

DOUG AND JAN HELLER love TV's *The Wheel of Fortune,* but don't have thirty spare minutes to watch it each night. So they've devised their own time-saving viewing method. They tape each program on their VCR and play it back soundlessly. Fast-freezing the first game board, they try to guess the answer with just the enumeration and category revealed. If they're unable to solve the puzzle with this barest of information they forward the tape to the spot where the first consonant has been filled in, stop the tape, and try again. This way they can "watch" the program in four minutes and solve all the puzzles.

As editor in chief and senior editor of Penny Press (publishers of 120 magazines and a dozen books a year) and parents of two young sons, the Hellers are truly teammates—sharing equally in their responsibilities at home and at work. They're remarkably similar in age and appearance—both are dark-haired, slender, and in their early thirties. Their busy schedules leave them with little time to themselves. Their idea of time off is to meet at a local coffee shop/bookstore where they can share a pot of imported coffee and solve the cryptic puzzle in *The Atlantic* together.

They have been teammates since they met at the University of Rochester; Doug recalls meeting Jan "when she was stood up on a date she had with my dorm next-door neighbor. I was sitting on my floor, solving a puzzle and listening to some Stephen Sondheim music. I invited her in and with these two interests in common—Sondheim and the puzzle—who needed a *deus ex machina*?"

Jan was a puzzle person from the time she was six years old, but her serious solving began with Doug, who was then constructing daily crosswords for *Campus Times,* the college newspaper, and bimonthly puzzles for the literary magazine. Jan helped Doug by test-solving his puzzles. During their courtship, engagement, and early married life they constructed puzzles for each other. Doug, on a cross-country trip, kept in touch with Jan by mailing crosswords to her from every stop. He remembers paying for a breakfast in a small Indiana town with a custom-made crossword puzzle for the owner of the bakery/diner he was in. His formal marriage proposal to Jan took the form of a treasure hunt: "She had to go from one puzzle to another, ending up with a cryptic that contained the proposal."

Before Jan and Doug tied the knot it was a must for her to learn to solve cryptic crosswords, for Doug was, and is, devoted to them. It was composer and cryptic constructor Stephen Sondheim, whose brilliant cryptics appeared in *New York* magazine, who first won Doug's interest.

The Hellers' puzzle careers are directly linked to that of Will Shortz (see page 200). When Shortz and Stephanie Spadaccini, former managing editor of *Games,* formed the Fairfield County Puzzlers (FCP), in Connecticut, they advertised for members in a Stamford newspaper. The Hellers, Stamford residents at that time, responded and began what's now a close friendship with Shortz. They're active members of the FCP, participate as judges at the Marriott and U.S. Open tournaments, and contribute clever word games and quizzes to *Games*. When Shortz left Penny Press to write his first *Brain Games* book, Doug replaced him, and has been an integral part of the growth spurt experienced by that company. When Penny Press moved its offices to Norwalk, Connecticut, the Hellers moved to nearby Weston.

Working for the same company eight hours a day seems to cause this couple no conflicts. Doug spends his time overseeing the day-to-day operations of the magazine staff of eight editors and more than twenty free-lancers. He solves whatever tough puzzle problems come up—in cluing, fact checking, fixing troublesome diagrams, etc. He's also responsible for getting all the magazines, as well as the books, published on a very tight production schedule.

Jan directs the editorial staff in preparing the puzzles they receive from constructors into the format necessary for publication. She chooses the material for every magazine and is in charge of all correspondence with constructors.

Correspondence is a very important part of any puzzle editor's work. Constructors usually work in a vacuum—creating puzzles at home in isolated environments—and want to know how editors feel about their work and when and where the accepted puzzles will appear in print. Most puzzle editors spend a great deal of time corresponding with constructors to make sure that their editorial needs are being met. Each publishing house has a stable of favorite constructors who regularly supply them with the puzzles needed for their magazines.

The Hellers don't have as much time as they'd like these days to solve or create puzzles, though they do occasionally join in a variation of a puzzle relay. One of them starts off by answering one clue which the other must use as a springboard to answering the next clue; e.g., if Doug fills in the grid with a five-letter answer to 1 Across, Jan must solve the clue in 1, 2, 3, 4, or 5 Down. Solving proceeds (rapidly) until the grid is filled in.

They have, however, created puzzles for *The Great Puzzle Catalog,* entered the Grossinger's contests (Doug won a chocolate crossword for his second-place finish), masterminded an elaborate treasure hunt for a "Britain Salutes New York Week" festival, and contributed puzzles to several crossword tournaments.

Their "Headlines" puzzle for the 1985 Great Western Tournament featured unfinished headlines with punny answers:

PAINT FACTORY HELD HOSTAGE; EMPLOYEES——	are marooned
FIRECRACKER SALES——	just booming
EIDER STOCK SOARS ON AMEX:——	now down is up
CARPET INVENTOR SAYS HE'S——	making a pile
SODA FOUNTAIN SALES ARE NO——	great shakes

The Hellers' "Going Too Far" crossword contained four extraneous squares in a 15×15 diagram. These horizontal entries were filled in by appropriate phrases—"my cup runneth over," "stick out at the ends," and "hang your head over."

As admirers of Stephen Sondheim, the Hellers honored him in the best way possible, by constructing a cryptic dedicated to his work. The puzzle was a feature of the 1983 Marriott tournament. Most of the clues related to Sondheim's Broadway shows, with these examples and explanations:

"Duelers in battle after opening of *Pacific Overtures*" = Preludes = p + reludes (anagram of duelers)

"In a comeback, Brynner has a big dance in *A Little Night Music*" = Lullaby = lu(llab)y (container/reversal)

"*Times* article on Sondheim's shows" = eons = articleE ON Sondheim's (hidden word)

"*Company* goes through sharp increases in misfortune" = scourge = s(co)urge (container)

"Walk to a new production of *Pirates*" = traipse (anagram of *Pirates*)

"Sondheim's eccentric devotion of pleasure" = hedonism (anagram of Sondheim)

"Story told: *Sunday in the Park* (unfinished) qualified" = parable = park + able (deletion/charade)

" 'Waltz' surrounds one in this case" = valise = val(i)se (container)

While a few solvers have complained that the Hellers' tournament puzzles are difficult, they have no cross words for this duo. And the Hellers themselves have nothing but kind words for the guy who stood Jan up that night they met so many years ago. Thanks to him, the world of crosswords is a lot brighter.

CRYPTIC CROSSWORD by Doug and Janis Heller

(SEE PAGE 262 FOR SOLUTION)

ACROSS

1 Morley is more secure (5)
4 Not absolute family member (8)
9 Strange vine mat for an Asian nation (7)
11 Drinker's sound is "in" and others find it corect (7)
12 Loud vow for the dog (4)
13 Destroy the id of Archie's wife (5)
14 Only fair (4)
17 It shows the way, a bit charged, feasted, and loving (13)
19 Hojo plans June bash for the admiral (4, 4, 5)
21 Island on the Cook's tour seen if I jiggle (4)
22 Bikini part in the mind (5)
23 Atmosphere or a sound (4)
26 Left Ken tuna salad (7)
27 Gain ire somehow in Africa (7)
28 Activate unit of an aquatic display (8)
29 Research found in model version (5)

DOWN

1 Safe cave reused to preserve one's dignity (4, 4)
2 Liberty fed more confusion (7)
3 Tore up the lease (4)
5 Form of murder to put into office or, the other way, cut a bit (13)
6 A revolutionary form of pain (4)
7 Clued in, you say? Flip and clue in (7)
8 Sparkle in the clatter (5)
10 The way it works is new: soldier's club for each (and me!) (5, 8)
15 Note the turning machine (5)
16 A musical instrument? Stop the little woman! (5)
18 Notice found inside: "Get away for an adventure" (8)
19 Self defense for just half . . . just half? It's inside! (7)
20 Real nut—looney—just doesn't care one way or the other (7)
21 A disease can get very loud for something inconsequential (5)
24 Sketch kit's in a mess (4)
25 French painter endlessly on the rise is old (4)

KAREN HODGE

WHEN KAREN HODGE competed in the 1979 Marriott crossword contest she was "very surprised to discover how good everyone was." Although she finished in the top half, she realized her limitations as a competitor and decided to venture into constructing—and in just a few years she has become a top constructor of cryptics and crosswords.

Hodge submitted her first 21×21 crossword to *Games*. It was returned almost immediately with a polite note from Will Shortz saying that *Games* didn't need any new constructors. Hodge, recognizing this as a polite rejection, put the puzzle aside for a few years. When she did resurrect and modify it, she sent it to Eugene T. Maleska at the *Times*. He rejected it too, but offered Hodge several helpful hints—stay away from overworked themes (Hodge had used geometric shapes—Bermuda Triangle, Trafalgar Square); don't use forced entries; keep the word count low; start off with a 15×15, not a 21×21 crossword. Hodge submitted several puzzles to Maleska, who although rejecting them, kept on encouraging her for he felt that she showed a flair for constructing.

Finally Hodge's perseverance paid off; it was a bird-theme puzzle—with "turkey trot," "round robin," "eagle eye," and "pigeon hole" entries—that won Maleska's acceptance. His congratulatory note, which elated her, began: "Your avian opus is certainly not for the birds."

In the year between acceptance of the puzzle and its publication in the daily *Times,* Hodge sold several puzzles to *Games* and *Four-Star Puzzler*. The latter was edited by Henry Rathvon and Emily Cox (see page 36) at this time; Rathvon used almost every puzzle Hodge submitted.

Hodge's outlets have expanded through the years: Her puzzles appear in the Dell *Champion* magazines, the Simon & Schuster books, and both Stanley Newman's (see page 128) and Henry Hook's (see page 66) Running Press series. Here are excerpts from several of Hodge's puzzles:

From "Pun Names":

Henry's dogs?	Feet of clay
Lucy in disguise?	Masked ball

From "Games":

Chess	Kind of pie
Poker	Fireside aid
Solitaire	Lone stone
Checkers	Nixon's dog
Dominoes	Half masks
Pool	Tide or steno

From "Canine Capers":

Cornmeal ball	Hush puppy
Popular folk music group	Irish rovers
Dressing way up	Putting on the dog
Comic strip duo	Mutt and Jeff
Instantly, like Johnny	On the spot

From "Name Game":

Call Shirley?	Telephone booth
Francis in Halloween get-up?	Skeleton key
Barbara's flowers?	Garden of Eden
Law-abiding Billie	Legal holiday
Flexible Terrence?	Rubber stamp
Joel, the snitch?	Tattletale gray
Cowards Patti and Geraldine?	Yellow pages
Little Sally	Short field

From "Up to Scratch":

Rubles?	Red cabbage
Stolen money?	Hot bread
Mad money?	Wild Bill
Tonight Show revenue	Johnny Cash
Finance committee?	Buckboard
Misers?	Doughnuts

From "Skoal":

Words to a hungover Zorba?	I told ouzo
Family of cognac connoisseurs?	The Brandy Bunch
Lee's tipsy songster?	Tequila mockingbird
Superb Italian daiquiri?	The glory that was rum
Thirsty Roman's request?	Ale Caesar

From "Wild Critters":

Bo-Peep's theme song	It had to be ewe
Biggest swine of them all?	Colossal boar

Hodge's decision to try a different puzzle route was prompted by Henry Rathvon. After listening to his speech on solving cryptics, presented just before the start of the 1983 Marriott cryptic contest (an adjunct to the regular crossword contest), Hodge created one of her own and mailed it to *Four-Star Puzzler*.

As she recalls now, Hodge "made every mistake in the book." Henry Rathvon's rejection letter included a four-page commentary evaluating every clue, pointing out the positive and negative aspects of each definition and entry. Hodge can't find enough good things to say about Rathvon for his encouragement, suggestions for improvement, and personal acceptance or rejection letters.

Anagramming is the wordplay used most often in cryptics; here are examples from Hodge's puzzles:

Saves Miracles hit	Reclaims
Completely wrecked great hotel	Altogether
Everything in revues failing	Universe
Rudely cuss Iran's egomaniac?	Narcissus
Display tattered Celt's cape	Spectacle

Anagrams in cryptics differ from those endorsed by the National Puzzler's League (NPL). According to the NPL, the perfect anagram "demands that the word or phrase evolved shall be equivalent in meaning to that whence it was derived." Examples from the NPL's files show how this criterion was met by various members through the years:

They see	The eyes
IX stand here	Three and six
Price speeds mail vastly	Special delivery stamps

Tender name	Endearment
Is not solaced	Disconsolate
A style of tribute	Statue of Liberty

John L. Hervey, writing in the NPL's *The Key to Puzzledom,* believed that one of the best verse anagrams ever composed was this one on "political leaders":

> The famous race is open,
> The entries duly made;
> The nation stands expectant
> Upon the grand parade.
> While sportive speculators
> Bet odds upon the field,
> The EDITORIAL SCALPEL
> The party organs wield.

A high-school French teacher in her early forties, the self-effacing Hodge seems surprised by her rapid rise from neophyte to superstar. Although she attends lots of puzzle tournaments, she tries to remain in the background and rarely, if ever, lets contestants know who she is. However, when and if her identity becomes known, contestants are always eager to talk to her about the puzzle business in general and her puzzles in particular.

Hodge's background really paved the way for her entry into the puzzle field. She's been solving puzzles since she was seven, developing skills with crosswords, anagrams, and any word puzzles she could find in *Child Life, My Weekly Reader,* and *Jack and Jill.* In fifth grade, she and a friend made their own crosswords although they "didn't know the first thing about symmetry, unkeyed letters, taboos on two-letter words, et cetera." However, "none of them ever reached the stage where anyone had to solve them." Her B.A. in French and M.A. in liberal studies (specializing in literature), gives her a broad background from which to draw in creating her diagrams and definitions, such as "contents of Trigger's feedbag?" for "oat cuisine."

Hodge does most of her constructing in the summer, working in her home office in Clinton, Connecticut. Her household includes her husband, Roy, and four dogs aged four to thirteen. Although her husband isn't a word person, he does give her good ideas which she uses as a springboard. The mental stimulation she derives in seeing a puzzle through from the germination of an idea to its send-off to an editor is one of the joys expressed by most constructors.

Solvers could use many words to describe Karen Hodge's puzzles. The one that comes most to mind is nine letters long, begins with "w," ends with "l," and means "marvelous"!

BENT SELLER LIST by Karen Hodge

(SEE PAGE 263 FOR SOLUTION)

ACROSS

1 *Raison d'*——
5 Beard site
9 Lou Grant's paper
13 Do a piper's job?
18 Lucy's neighbor
19 Splitsville
20 Pervasive quality
21 Napoleon on Elba
22 *Nemo's Hope?*
25 One of Wally's buddies
26 Arrange systematically
27 Held on to
28 Tater
30 Organic compound
31 Berry and Howard
33 Woman's magazine
35 Folksinger of the 60s
39 "Look ——, I'm . . ."
41 *Ms. Dennis Sprains an Ankle?*
44 Fireplace shelf
45 Pert
47 Parts of an organism
48 Mischievous one
49 Storm center
50 On vacation
51 *Irving Wallace: A Biography?*
58 Small one
59 20th-century emperor
61 Saarinen
62 Destructive
64 Yoko and family
65 Schoolteacher, country-style
67 Makes a lawn
69 Bud's supporter
70 Jannings
72 Let out
74 Less than grosses
76 Gets long in the tooth
78 Suds
80 Ham's dad
82 "Little" girl of the comics
84 "Clue" weapon
86 Impediment
89 Daughter of Uranus and Gaea
91 Imaginary
93 Rhoda's mother
94 *Pentagon Personnel?*
97 104 wks., minimum
98 Ms. Russell, familiarly
99 —— Marie Saint
100 *Our Hearts Were Young and* ——
101 Be a ham
103 *Dernier* ——
104 *Adam, Eve, and the Snake?*
108 Bridges
109 Hagar's headgear
111 Rich Little, for one
112 Enthusiasm
114 First of the James Bond movies
117 She was born free
119 *Star Wars* creature
121 Took a trip
123 —— and end-all
126 *Champagne Thief?*
129 Island off Venezuela
130 Change for a five
131 —— -O (song refrain)
132 Torch-bearer Johnson
133 Senegal's capital
134 Pub projectile
135 Ending with omni or insecti
136 Words from the pros?

DOWN

1 One Allen
2 *South American Reptiles?*
3 Outcome
4 Last month of the Jewish year
5 Box
6 Treasure State's capital
7 Officeholders
8 Cranny's partner
9 Chinese capital
10 Steal veal?
11 Anger
12 Baritone's inferior?
13 Trick
14 Emit
15 Edge
16 Mont Blanc, for one
17 *Daughter of Time* author
18 Ending for kitchen or din
23 Use a kiln
24 Puts in other words
29 Like a stuffed shirt
32 She played Leather on "Happy Days"
34 *Gendarme,* slangily
36 *Ralph Edwards Presents?*
37 "Happy Birthday ——"
38 Assists in villainy
40 Legend
42 Winning margin, in the Derby
43 Cupid
45 N.Y. area south of Houston Street
46 "This is —— how-do-you-do!"
52 White House beagle
53 List ender, sometimes
54 Best Actress of 1961
55 Bridges-Boxleitner sci-fi flick
56 Sing à la Swiss
57 "——, Juanita . . ."
60 Wickerwork material
63 Actress Pola
66 New Zealand native
68 Nonsense
71 —— *-motif*
73 Comedienne Madeline
75 Cole's follower
77 Gush
79 Uses the microwave
81 Shrubbery, often

83 St. George's sweetheart (*Faerie Queen*)
85 Otherwise
86 Gray or paper
87 Idolize
88 Guns
90 "A song of love is —— song . . ."
92 Algonquin Indian
95 —— Hari
96 Hear, courtroom-style
102 Cleared a path
104 Storm or root
105 First bidder
106 Least
107 Infernal
108 Lacking zip
110 Kind of toast
113 Bandleader Shaw
115 Geese of Oahu
116 Baltic Sea feeder
118 ". . . in apprehension, how like ——!" *(Hamlet)*
120 Chicken ——
122 Miles
123 Like Leroy Brown
124 Epoch
125 Penguin-like bird
127 "Ode —— Grecian Urn"
128 Uruguayan uncle

HENRY HOOK

HENRY HOOK HAS such a flair for defining clues that he seems to be an astronaut circling a globe of words with the unique ability to view them from angles unavailable to those on earth. Who else could come up with these clues (or as Hook might crack, "Who else would want to?"):

Facial phooeys	Sneers
Just hang there	Droop
Extra in a Weissmuller film?	Ape
They take great interest in their work	Usurers
Chopping spree?	Karate
Ewe kid?	Lamb
Bet middler	Bookie
Mobile home?:abbr.	Ala.
Crayola's 64, e.g.?	Hues
The Midas touch?	Greed
See red?	Owe

Hook has dim memories of solving criss-cross types of puzzles (clueless puzzles presented with a grid and a list of words to be placed inside) as a child. Since he "never purchased a newspaper that didn't have funnies," he certainly didn't polish his solving skills on the *Times* puzzle as did so many other constructors. Yet it was a soon-to-be *Times* editor, Eugene T. Maleska, who first spotted Hook's genius.

Hook had been doodling with crosswords for some years when he received a gift of a jigsaw crossword created by Maleska. The finished puzzle with its Stepquote message—"You have just solved the world's greatest puzzle"—inspired Hook to draft his own response—"What makes you think your puzzle is greater than mine?"—in a crossword. He mailed it to Maleska, c/o Dell Publishing Company in New York City, not realizing that Maleska lived just down the road from him in New Jersey. Maleska was sufficiently impressed with Hook's raw talent to offer to critique his crosswords and send him a style sheet (which Hook hadn't known existed).

The rules that Margaret Farrar was so instrumental in developing—allover interlocking, symmetry, limiting black squares to one sixth of the diagram, and no two-letter words—are still adhered to by most puzzle editors and constructors. Each publication also has its own style sheet for constructors to follow when submitting puzzles.

Hook knew most of these rules when he started sending puzzles to Maleska, but quickly learned that not every dictionary entry is valid for use in a puzzle. Farrar's primary rule, still in effect, was that puzzles were a recreational activity and should be fun to solve. She banned words relating to war, disease, death, and other unsavory subjects, for she firmly believed that people solved puzzles to escape their problems. She always quipped that "if solvers are trying to figure out the answer to Seven Down they can't be worrying about how to pay the rent."

As Hook developed under Maleska's tutelage, Maleska further assisted him by sending his work to other editors. In just a short while Hook was selling his puzzles to Margaret Farrar (the *Los Angeles Times* Syndicate), Herb Ettenson (the *Chicago Tribune* Syndicate), Rosalind Moore (Dell Publishing Company), and Will Weng (*The New York Times*). Hook is one of the few constructors whose first published crossword appeared in the *Times*.

Hook earned all his spending money at college by selling crosswords. He also constructed clued criss-cross types of puzzles for his classmates to solve. It was also during his college years that Hook developed his versions of TV game shows. He would crib questions from the shows and act as emcee in the student lounge. Years later, when Hook joined the NPL, he found an even more receptive audience for his games. At the Syracuse convention in 1979 Hook held fifty members captive with his version of *The $20,000 Pyramid* with die-hard league members even forgoing sleep to play the game.

Hook continued to sell crosswords after graduating from William Paterson College in New Jersey, but the income he derived from puzzles was still his secondary source of funds. Puzzles were "something to come home to" after work. At this time (1977) there just wasn't enough money in the business to be self-supporting on crosswords alone.

But puzzles became his primary career when *Games* magazine started its spin-off, *The Four-Star Puzzler,* in 1981 and Will Shortz hired Hook as editor. He filled its pages with cryptic crosswords, logic problems, rebus cartoons, cryptograms, word contests, and outrageous quizzes. An expert on trivia, Hook can answer 75 to 90 percent of all the questions on game shows, but has never appeared on one. He did audition for *The $20,000 Pyramid,* but wasn't asked to be a contestant, undoubtedly because he answered all the questions correctly. He'll figure out the solution on *Wheel of Fortune* seconds after the puzzle outline is shown and category is announced.

Hook gathered unusual material from numerous sources to compose deadly quizzes for *Four-Star*'s readers. Examples of his broad range of knowledge show up in these questions (answers are on page 74):

- Would a doctor, a surveyor, or a meteorologist make the best use of a sphygmomanometer?
- A Maryland preacher named Mason Weems created a piece of folklore concerning the quasi-malicious destruction of a woody plant of the genus *Prunus*. Who is the subject of this legend?
- Sheepdogs are trained to herd and guard sheep. Sled dogs are trained to pull Eskimo sleds. What are firedogs useful for?
- What fruit has its seeds on the outside?

Cryptograms in *Four-Star,* created by Sally Porter, were designed especially to "suppress letter frequencies and alter letter patterns." More difficult than those in traditional puzzle publications, they also reflected the magazine's off-beat humor:

> "It is not necessarily true that good things come in small packages. So do subpoenas and income tax forms."
>
> "Newlywed pranksters prepare for inevitable shivaree, spiking sassafras libations with white lightning."
>
> "Stir-fry cook quakes from queer, horrific dream: teriyaki scorched, green onion squishy, soy sauce sour."

When *Four-Star* folded, Hook continued to construct and edit on a free-lance basis, as he still does today. Working at home "slaving over a hot typewriter" not only "cuts down on commuting time," but allows him to watch *The $100,000 Pyramid, Super Password, Wheel of Fortune, Scrabble, Jeopardy,* and other game shows practically all day. Hook uses game shows as his reference sources and gathers numerous tidbits of information to clue familiar words differently or to put unusual words in his diagrams:

—— -no-yu (Japanese tea ceremony)	Cha
Millet's man has one	Hoe
Frequent *Gong Show* panelist	Reed
Wilbur's steed	Mr. Ed
One of Donald's boys	Dewey
Compete in a roleo	Birl
Tatum O'Neal's Oscar role	Addie

Hook never uses a dictionary to define words; he relies on the treasury of knowledge stored in his brain and the ability to look at words in a different way from everybody else. Solvers of his crosswords know always to expect the unexpected from him.

Hook is one of the regular suppliers of crosswords at tournaments. Participants groan audibly when his puzzles appear, for they know they'll have to solve clues like these from his "Black and White" puzzle at the 1983 U.S. Open:

Part of a black-and-white	Chocolate sauce
What's black and white ——?	And red all over
Artwork in black and white	Chiaroscuro
Some are black-and-white	Television sets
Black-and-white, as some fabrics	Zebra-striped

The three top finalists in the First North Jersey Crossword Open were challenged with Hook's "Last Words" crosswords containing "a little bit of everything, with clues to confuse." Examples show just how true this subtitle was:

Wheels of fortune?	Limousine
Pods?	Pea jackets
Run-on preventive	Space bar
Senorita's curves?	Tilde
Pony	Fluid ounce
Pocketful, but not of rye	Pita

Hook was on the other end of the tournament scene in 1981, when he easily won the third Ridgewood, New Jersey, Newspapers Tournament, breezing through four puzzles in just twenty-nine minutes. The rapidity with which he filled in the diagrams astonished even veteran contestants like Miriam Raphael and Joel

Darrow. Hook felt his "adrenaline revving up during the first crossword" and never downshifted through the rest of the contest. Tournament directors Will Shortz and Stanley Newman have effectively kept Hook from entering any other tournaments by commissioning him to construct one of the tournament crosswords, judge the contest, and/or act as co-organizer.

Hook's unofficial role at tournaments and conventions is that of resident wit. He's a big fellow, more than six feet tall, and has a lot of physical presence. In all his thirty-four years he can count the number of times he's worn a suit. He is always dressed casually. One of his regular tournament outfits is a T-shirt imprinted with a tuxedo jacket which he wears for the formal awards dinner. His sense of humor coupled with his speedy retorts has no equal in the puzzle world. When several judges were brainstorming clues for a humorous puzzle with a photography theme, Hook came up with these expressions—"Chaim a Camera," "Old Focus at Home," "F Stop Fitzgerald," and "Eyefish I Were in Dixie." At the first Baltimore convention, while attendees were playing a group game based on "water" words (e.g., "Waterford crystal," "*Watership Down*"), Hook yelled out, "Water we doing here?"

Hook is one of only a handful of constructors who are adept at creating cryptic crosswords, and his anagrams (traditionally the easiest parts of cryptics) reflect his ability to rearrange words creatively:

"Midwesterners win, so a regrouping is called for" = IOWANS (win, so a)

"The mule has bucked an old man" = METHUSELAH (the mule has)

"Hotel suite's macabre shadow" = SILHOUETTE (hotel suite)

"Changes new med roles" = REMODELS (med roles)

"Yes eight changes make sense" = EYESIGHT (yes eight)

"Call a GI terribly cold" = GLACIAL (call a GI)

" 'Strict economy is,' I say, 'utter chaos' " = AUSTERITY (I say, utter)

Hook is even more devious when he uses container clues, in which one word encloses another. Containers always give some indication of enclosure, e.g., "Scoundrel, in time, will make mistakes": RAT (scoundrel) goes in ERA (time) to produce ERRATA (mistakes). Here are some of Hook's container clues:

Helps one getting into commercials	A(i)ds
The group has a choice idea	The(or)y
Post office has stolen picture	P(hot)o
Malodorous ink in pens	St(ink)y

Hook is such a master at using multiple types of wordplay in his cryptics that few solvers expect to breeze through them. Typical Hook clues (typical in the level of difficulty) require multiple thought processes: "Fancy dress worn by more than three leggy creatures" yields "spiders." Solvers would be expected to reason along these lines: Anagram ("fancy") dress; enclose the rearranged word ("worn by") around pi ("more than three") to determine spiders ("leggy creatures").

Solvers would also have to recognize a charade/reversal clue in "Serbian victory . . . and man returns." The answer, "Yugoslav," breaks down into YUG (man + OSLA (and) + V (victory) with all parts of the charade reversed.

To solve Hook's cryptics one must look at all the meanings of a word, not take anything at face value, beware of misleading punctuation, and think creatively. Always remember that Hook uses no extraneous words in his clues; thus, a complete analysis of a clue will show how each word in the definition leads to the solution. Hook clued "designer" as: "Couturier giving autograph inside—one buck."

- COUTURIER is the the straight definition (designer)
- GIVING indicates the straight clue is equal to the wordplay clue that follows
- AUTOGRAPH is "sign"
- INSIDE means the wordplay is a container type
- ONE BUCK is "deer"

Similarly, solvers can understand Hook's logic by analyzing the following answers and relating them to the clues:

"A den he remodeled is a knockout?" = ANESTHESIA—a + nest + he + sia (*is a* anagram)

"Polish cars vigorously with Henry and Grant" = SCHOLARSHIP—sc(h)olarship (anagram of *polish cars* around "H" for Henry)

"51-pound convertible" = LIQUID—LI (51) + quid (pound)

Solvers who mistook buck for money, Grant for a proper name, and convertible for car weren't thinking like Hook.

Hook also creates rebuses for Dell's *Champion* line of puzzle magazines. Hook spent the "best years of my childhood" watching *Concentration,* the long-running game show that revolved around rebuses of slogans, names, or places. Hook's dreams of being a contestant on the show were squashed when, just as he became eligible to audition (contestants had to be at least eighteen years old), the show was discontinued.

Rebuses for *Concentration* were created by Norm Blumenthal, a genial artist-showman, who specialized in "bending and twisting the English language." For example, F + I+ N + Doors + Key + Purse + Lew + Saws + We + Purse translates to "Finders keepers, losers weepers" and R + Owl + F + Wall + Toe + Hammer + Sun = "Ralph Waldo Emerson."

Hook's rebuses for Dell involve adding and subtracting pictures to form new words, e.g., Ankle + R − Rake + Moose − Lemon + Cars = Oscars.

In contrast, letter rebuses are an old standby in the National Puzzlers' League, whose members delight in mystifying one another. Solutions to the following puzzles are based on letter placements, the number of letters in the rebus, or missing letters:

HHHHHHHH = Octaves
(*answer*: eight H's; eighths)

BCDEFGIJKLMNOPQRSTUVWXYZ = Bible hero
(*answer*: No A, H; Noah)

RRRRRRR
RRRRRRR
RRRRRRR
RRRRRRR
RRRRRRR
RRRRRRR
RRRRRRR
(*answer*: Forty-nine R's: forty-niners

M
E
(*answer*: an em on E; anemone)

Rebus historians believe that a letter addressed with these three little words:

WOOD
JOHN
MASS

was delivered to its owner, John Underwood, Andover, Mass., without any trouble.

Two famous lines from Shakespeare were depicted in rebus form by the master puzzler Sam Loyd (answers are on page 74):

Hook's puzzles appear in *Games* magazine, the Dell *Champion* puzzle magazines and *The Crossworder's Own Newsletter*. He also edits crossword collections for various publishers, constructs puzzles for most of the major crossword contests, and co-organizes tournaments with Stan Newman.

Hook's wife, Stephanie Abrams-Hook, shares his total involvement in crosswords. Hook met her at a mini-NPL convention in Boston and courted her long-distance (he was living in New Jersey at the time) with rebus puzzles (in the style of *Concentra-*

tion) and crosswords. Hook's contribution of his seven hundred reference books to their joint library undoubtedly played an important role in Abrams-Hook's decision to construct her own crosswords. Her talent was recognized early as she began to sell her puzzles almost immediately. Hook refers to himself as her "live-in librarian," a role he's extremely happy to play.

Henry Hook, with his knowledge of general trivia ("I served under him for three years," quips Hook), flair for defining words, prodigious output, and ready wit, brightens up the black and white world of crosswords as no one else.

ANSWERS—HOOK

Trivia

1. A doctor—that's the gadget he'd wrap around your arm to check your blood pressure.
2. George Washington, chopping down the cherry tree
3. For holding logs; they're andirons.
4. Strawberry

Sam Loyd Rebuses

1. All's well that ends well.
2. To be or not to be.

NINES AND FIVES by Henry Hook

(SEE PAGE 263 FOR SOLUTION)

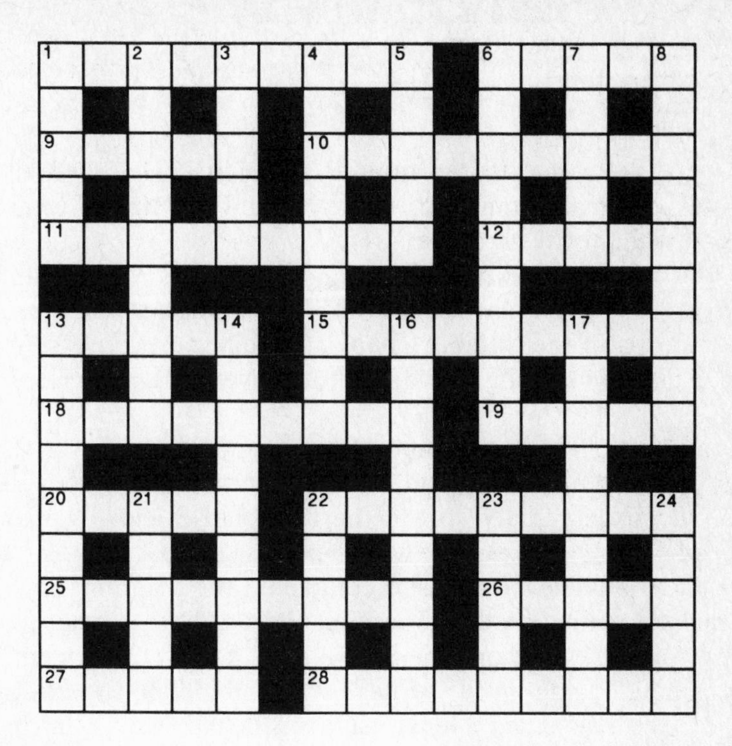

ACROSS

1 Desires a quiet little Sunday (9)
6 Accommodate either way? (3, 2)
9 Laborer kidnaps Queen Eva of Argentina (5)
10 Back-row shuffle (9)
11 Solving for four points in a circle (9)
12 Recitation of Frost! (5)
13 Heavens!—schusses around Everest's peak (5)
15 Horse and rodent, back in first place, named for someone (9)
18 A bit of soap, in small measures, removes oil (9)
19 Parcel of land gets us a plant (5)
20 Left bus station and had a drink (5)
22 Ready-made to cover the ear (9)
25 Cheer about plain school in Pennsylvania (9)
26 After one Italian entree, . . . (5)
27 . . . photograph a rocket launch (5)
28 Performers with a hundred locks (9)

DOWN

1 Mountain height abbreviated by a Greek letter (5)
2 Dying general has one (9)
3 "Fasten Seat Belts"—nervous? (5)
4 Quality of the latest Streisand medley (9)
5 Gave evidence about long, informal speech (5)
6 Picture sunlight through doorway (9)
7 Inferior time in New York (5)
8 Nobles seen stripped, placed in irons (9)
13 I see TV ads pitching tranquilizers (9)
14 Firm shows failure—in terrible, sad state (9)
16 Watchful butler follows obstetrician (9)
17 They hope to pick one loser outside track's entrance (9)
21 Explorer contracts one illness (5)
22 Florida has choice plant life (5)
23 Remove head from specimen—it's enough (5)
24 Pulls ties (5)

MAURA JACOBSON

A SERIOUS AUTOMOBILE accident in 1971 forced Maura Jacobson to remain immobile for a year and she turned to crosswords to while away the time.

Jacobson actually started solving crosswords when she was eleven years old. Her father, an avid solver, let her have first try at the puzzles in the Sunday *Times* and daily newspapers. When she had filled in all she could, he took over and completed the puzzle.

Jacobson never thought about constructing until a serendipitous occasion when she found herself with two copies of a daily *Times*. Jacobson rapidly solved the first puzzle and filled in the blanks of the second puzzle with her own words. Starting with her husband's name (Jerry) she completed the diagram, clued it, and brazenly mailed it off to Margaret Farrar. At that time, Jacobson, unaware that all words had to be bona fide dictionary entries, had concocted some words of her own to complete the grid. For example, she had clued "hime" as "residence: var." Farrar, of course, immediately understood what Jacobson had done, but graciously wrote that she "had looked everywhere and couldn't find 'hime' and would reconsider the puzzle if certain changes were made." Jacobson revised the puzzle several times and saw her first construction printed in the daily *Times*. Her goal then became to have a puzzle in the Sunday *Times*. After achieving that distinction a few times she stopped constructing.

But the accident left her with time on her hands when she couldn't be on her feet and she decided to rekindle her constructing skills. Going through her puzzle files she realized that one of the puzzles she had sent to Farrar had never been published. Her letter to Farrar's successor, Will Weng, requesting information about the lost puzzle was forwarded to Farrar, who, finding out that Jacobson was in the hospital, sent her graph paper to use for her diagrams. It was the best get-well present Jacobson ever received, for it marked the beginning of the second chapter of Jacobson's illustrious crossword career.

For most of the seventies Jacobson's puzzles appeared in the *Times,* the Simon & Schuster series, the *L.A. Times* Syndicate, and various other publications. When the editors of *Cue* magazine wanted to start a regular puzzle column in 1978 they asked Will Weng to create a brand-new crossword for each issue. Weng declined and recommended Jacobson instead. Her puzzles were so popular that when *New York* magazine bought *Cue* two years later and dropped the puzzle, a flood of protesting letters (including one from Jacobson's mother-in-law) forced the publishers to reconsider their hasty decision and reinstate the puzzle. The puzzle was absent from only three issues.

Solvers associate Jacobson, more than any other constructor, with funny, punny clues and they look to her crosswords, especially at tournaments, to amuse them. They're never disappointed.

Jacobson doesn't think of herself as a punster and claims that only one out of five *New York* crosswords is punny. But clues from various Jacobson masterpieces show why she's been dubbed the "queen of puns."

From "Movies You May Have Missed" at the 1978 First Annual American Crossword Puzzle Tournament:

Why the Five-Year Plan succeeded	Ivanhoed
Musical sequel to *Jaws*	Porgy and Bass
Venus's shortcomings exposed	Farewell Two Arms
Post-Watergate depression	Mopy Dick

From "Loaded Questions" at the 1984 U.S. Open:

Star of *Forty Clarets*?	Lynn Redgrape
Heady Youngman colleague?	Tipsey Russell
Souse Poll canvasser?	Elmo Toper
Snort-order cook?	Betty Crocked

From "Peoples Are Funny" in Series 133 of the Simon & Schuster books:

Tony Orlando hit?	Thai a Yellow Ribbon
Words from a *South Pacific* song?	Nothing Like a Dane
Song from *The Music Man*?	Marian the Liberian
Advice from Irving Berlin?	Lett Yourself Go

From "Is There a Doctor in the House?" at the 1986 Presenting Baltimore Annual Crossword Open:

Ailment contracted from a convertible sofa	Castroenteritis
Liver disorder of cows	Heifertitis
Cramps experienced in expensive cars	Mercedes bends
Abnormal fear of the Taj Mahal	Agraphobia

From "Greetings!" at the 1986 Stamford Marriott Tournament:

Greeting from Julia Ward's marshland?	Howes bayou
Landlubber's greeting?	Long time no sea
Museum greeting?	Arty welcome
Aloha?	Hello Hawaii

For the final puzzle in the 1979 Marriott tournament Jacobson treated solvers to a unique "Questionnaire" with clues like these:

What results from embassy vaccinations?	Diplomatic immunity
What do New England barbers use?	Yankee clippers
What kind of jam is made in the jungle?	Wildlife preserves
What does the Capitol otologist check?	Senate hearing
What concerns thrifty horses?	Stable economy
Where do Julius' fans sit?	Caesarean sections
What does Travolta do on the beach?	John browns body

Although Jacobson, a dark-haired, petite woman, is barely five feet tall, she dwarfs almost everyone else at crossword tournaments. She's witty and charming and tournamentgoers regularly flock to her. Although she refuses to referee a solving round in which her puzzle is featured, she is interested in knowing how solvers react to it. The results are always gratifying: The noise level usually rises several decibels during a Jacobson puzzle round as solvers chuckle when they fill in the grid with punny answers. (Jacobson is popular among her peers, too. When Eugene T. Maleska conducted an informal survey of the top constructors, they chose Jacobson as their favorite.)

Jacobson relies on numerous references to construct the sixty puzzles she produces each year. When she started editing a crossword series (*Crossword Puzzles with Themes*) she found that she needed to expand her reference collection. Working with other people's puzzles was an eye-opener for Jacobson, who hadn't realized all the hard work that goes into changing clues, altering diagrams, and checking facts.

She constructs slowly, taking as many as twenty hours to produce a 21×21 crossword. She feels that "constructing is really solving a puzzle—getting words to fit a theme." She enjoys working alone at home, because she has the ability to make her own schedule. This flexibility allows her to spend a lot of time with her husband and to travel to England every other year to visit her daughter, son-in-law, and grandson.

Jacobson jots down theme ideas on scraps of paper and throws them into an envelope. She literally reaches into a bag of tricks when she needs inspiration for a crossword. Although she's most recognized for her American-style crossword, she composed a "Cryptic Mix" puzzle for Series 126 in the Simon & Schuster collection. Definitions in this puzzle were an olio of puns and anagrams and cryptic clues:

The RAF returns before love game	Faro
Avoid Brubeck back east	Evade
Stick a commercial on this spot	Adhere
In charge of the chief expenses	Overhead
Output at 235 Madison Avenue	Ads
When pressed, I drone peculiarly	Ironed

Phyllis McGinley, a writer of humorous verse, proposed several suggestions to elevate the role of crosswords in American society:

- Create a Cabinet post with a Secretary in Charge of Puzzles.
- Set a standard for crosswords, like those used for food and weight.
- Require every newspaper to publish a daily crossword and a Sunday crossword that would cover an entire page and take all afternoon to complete.
- Form a guild for composers to learn the craft of crossword constructing.
- Award Guggenheim fellowships to promising designers.

McGinley's rules would be welcomed by crossword addicts everywhere. And the first person to whom they'd award a Guggenheim would probably be Maura Jacobson, puzzledom's proof that "the pun is mightier than the sword."

WHO'S THAT AGAIN? by Maura Jacobson

(SEE PAGE 263 FOR SOLUTION)

ACROSS

1 Captain's post
5 They place "wanted" ads
8 "—— fan tutte"
12 Virgil's colleague
16 This-and-that at the dinnertable
17 Outward image
18 Black-border news item
19 City north of Tahoe
20 OAS member
21 Opera star who is a pill
24 Squeaky-voiced czar
26 Gung-ho
27 Third word of "America"
28 Start of a countdown
29 Back of a book
31 New "Angel" Roberts
34 Apple polisher of the PLO
39 Resting upon
40 "—— Universe"
42 Is privy to
43 Yorkshire river
44 "Happy ——"
46 "The Waste Land" author
48 Soprano Gluck
49 More intricate
51 Cockney SOS
52 Unit of work
54 Actress who appeared too long in *Camille*
58 East Coast highway route
59 The lady
60 "Your days are ——"
63 Envelope abbr.
66 Thickheaded
68 Rubdown expert
69 Couple
70 Spanish waters
72 The third of "36-24-36"
74 Flicka, but not Mr. Ed
75 A real sweetheart of a barbarian
78 Took part in a poll
79 Stradivari's teacher
80 —— Nova
81 Needlefish
82 Ottoman sultan
84 Air Force general, flyer of heckicopters
91 Friend of Wyatt Burp
93 Golfer's target
94 Kin of curare
95 Modern women's magazine
96 Salt Lake City players
97 Dill, old style
98 Spreads hay
99 Botanist Gray et al.
100 Partner of feathers
101 Frequent city cry

DOWN

1 Pueblo Indian
2 Alt.
3 Calabria coin
4 Cavalry cop who always gets his snake
5 Word with single and nail
6 Actors Warren and Ned
7 Augment
8 Ty of baseball
9 Agora coin
10 Profile view
11 Meiji statesman
12 Amadis' love
13 Vindictive
14 *Bus Stop* dramatist
15 "Let's Make a Deal" choice
17 Speed abbrs.
22 Poetic twilights
23 Golda's family
25 Padre's sister
30 Fido's foot
31 Kind of top
32 Egyptian sun disk
33 "—— never"
35 Finesse
36 Closed
37 Kind of wrestling
38 Afternoon quaff
40 One-time election indicator
41 In high dudgeon
45 Windsor's neighbor
47 Glass ovens
48 Actress having problems with a bouffant hairdo
50 That old school spirit
52 Lazarus and Bovary
53 Adam's and spare
55 Nursery rhyme porridge
56 Andy of the comics
57 Adjective for Alfred
61 Normandy department
62 Book by Stowe
63 Oklahoma oil city
64 Museum superstar of 1979
65 Wracked up, as a car
66 Manicurists' concerns
67 Quicker way
70 As meek as ——
71 Hood's weapon
73 Bugs: Latin
76 Ammonia derivatives
77 Spydom VIP
78 Ms. Harper, to friends
81 Scams
82 Alda's costar
83 "—— Kleine Nachtmusik"
85 Stewpot
86 Radio transmission abbrs.
87 Plaintiff
88 Leonardo lady
89 Haley of *Roots* fame
90 Himalayan figure
92 "This —— recording"

1 2 3 4 5 6 7 8 9 10 11 12 13 14 15
16 17 18 19
20 21 22 23
24 25 26
27 28 29 30
31 32 33 34 35 36 37 38
39 40 41 42 43
44 45 46 47 48
49 50 51 52 53
54 55 56 57
58 59 60 61 62
63 64 65 66 67 68
69 70 71 72 73 74
75 76 77 78
79 80 81
82 83 84 85 86 87 88 89 90
91 92 93
94 95 96 97
98 99 100 101

STAN KURZBAN

DON'T USE INK when you're solving a Stan Kurzban diagramless puzzle—you not only have to figure out its clues, but you also have to reconstruct the diagram. Kurzban specializes in pictographic diagramlesses: the completed puzzle, not always symmetrical, forms a recognizable shape related to the thematic entries.

His masterpieces, most of which have appeared in the Sunday *New York Times,* include puzzles in the shape of a football, a Star of David, a map of New York State, a heart, and the letters SOS. Eugene T. Maleska, accepting the last of these, explained: "Because your SOS diagram is so clever, I will violate a rule that Margaret Farrar laid down for me years ago—'Puzzles are a form of escape; never use a downbeat theme.' " Kurzban's entries were downbeat indeed—Earhart (Amelia), Mary (Deare), Roberto (Clemente), Andrea (Doria), *Lusitania, Titanic,* snipers, and Mayday.

His heart-shaped crossword was published one February with, of course, a center that read "Happy Saint Valentine's Day." The Star of David puzzle contained these thematic entries—Israelite, Solomons, Genesis V, worships, synagogue, torahs, Mogen Davids, and Jewish stars. His New York State puzzle was highly praised in Maleska's *Across and Down:* "In Will Weng's day the ultimate in shaping diagramless puzzles was reached by Stanley A. Kurzban. The outline of New York State appeared and inside the puzzle chief cities like Utica . . . and New York were located exactly where they are on a map."

Kurzban also created all the puzzles in the *Star Trek Puzzle Manual.* For one whose theme was "Vulcan," Mr. Spock's home planet, solvers were able to see Spock's face in the completed diagram.

A computer scientist for IBM, Kurzban is a serious, intense man in his mid-forties. He lives with his wife and three children in Poughkeepsie, New York. He started solving the crossword puzzles in the *Miami Herald* when he was ten years old. His father and brother were also solvers. His constructing days, however, didn't begin until the mid-seventies, after he met professional puzzlesmith Mel Rosen, also of IBM.

Kurzban and Rosen were substitute players in the same lunch-hour bridge game. When Kurzban asked for some constructing advice, Rosen was happy to clue him in to the tricks of the trade.

Like many constructors, Kurzban started off with a 21×21 crossword and mailed it to Will Weng, who promptly rejected it. Kurzban had misinterpreted the *Times*'s style sheet and used the maximum words permissible for a 23×23 crossword in his smaller version. He quickly learned the rules, revised the puzzle, and resubmitted it to Weng, who was happy to accept it.

Once Kurzban mastered the initial steps, he started selling crosswords on a regular basis. He and his friend Rosen, feeling that there had to be a way to make more money from crosswords, approached Springbok Game Company with an idea to personalize puzzles. Their approach was to leave one corner of a crossword blank and use information from purchasers to make that portion of the diagram unique for them. When Springbok vetoed this idea, Kurzban and Rosen turned their thoughts to writing a book.

They developed an outline for a book on composing and solving crossword puzzles and mailed proposals to several logical publishers, e.g., those already publishing puzzle books or series. Again, they were rejected.

At this time, Kurzban, author of an already published college textbook for computer science, proposed a second edition of his book to his editor at Van Nostrand Reinhold Company. Almost as an afterthought he "threw the crossword puzzle book proposal into the same envelope." The rest, as they say, is how publishing history is made, for the publisher rejected the first proposal but gave the go-ahead to the puzzle-book project.

Sharing the writing fifty-fifty, Kurzban and Rosen produced *The Compleat Cruciverbalist or How to Solve and Compose Crossword Puzzles for Fun and Profit*. The book, published in both hardcover and paperback, was a moneymaker for both authors. Although it's now out of print, Kurzban and Rosen hope the publishers will reissue it in the near future.

Kurzban's chapter on solving diagramlesses takes solvers step by step (complete with diagrams) through the necessary motions.

He advises solvers to start with 1 Across, whose "length is always one less than the number of the second answer Across"; for example, if the second Across clue is numbered 5, the answer to the first Across clue contains four letters.

Kurzban eschews the conventional grids because they're not large enough. Since much of diagramless solving is trial and error, he advises solvers to use their own grids and make sure that they're larger than the finished diagram will be.

Other solving hints include putting numbers in each square that starts a word; placing black squares before and after each word; and using the symmetrical nature of crosswords to guide you; for example, once you've figured out the diagram at the top of the grid, turn it upside down and construct the same diagram on the bottom. The symmetry hint is valid only for those puzzles that have conventional symmetry (top to bottom) or left-right symmetry. However, some classic diagramless puzzles are not symmetrical, for they form a unique shape related to the theme of the puzzle itself.

The "invention" of the diagramless puzzle came about in a nonconventional way. During the crossword craze in 1924, Margaret Farrar, Prosper Buranelli, and F. Gregory Hartswick were eating lunch and editing puzzles at a New York restaurant when they realized that the grid was missing for one of the puzzles. Hartswick, using the back of a menu, whipped up the diagram in no time at all and *voilà!* the diagramless was born.

Clues for the first diagramless, published in *The New York World* on May 18, 1924, didn't stray far from the typical formula of those times, e.g., 1–5 "The best part of a thing" (cream); 6–8 "a quill" (pen); 9–13 "warmth of affection" (flame).

When Farrar started editing the *New York Times* crossword she included a diagramless puzzle every fourth week. Both Weng and Maleska have continued this practice.

Kurzban's skills are by no means limited to diagramless puzzles. He's used clever entries and themes in traditional puzzles. In one, he fitted directional words into their appropriate spaces in the grid, e.g., "right for the part" on the right side, "middle of the road" in the center, etc.

For a puzzle with a numbers theme, his clues were very precise: 17 Across was clued as "What this is and how it goes" and was answered by "Seventeen across." Similarly, 1 Across was clued as "What this would be in Germany" and answered by "eine."

Kurzban's wife, Nina, typed the manuscript for his book and all of his puzzles except one. Kurzban wanted to surprise her with a special puzzle he had created in honor of her birthday. Since Kurzban knew the date of publication, he suggested that Nina "look at the puzzle" on that day. The four different clues for Nina—"girl in Spanish," "Columbus's ship," "Ms. Simone," and "Ms. Foch"—clued her in to the constructor's identity.

Kurzban majored in mathematics and information sciences in college (Tulane) and graduate school (Syracuse University), but draws upon his extensive vocabulary and knowledge of French, Latin, and German when constructing. He begins with a theme and selects the longest theme-related words for the first entries in the puzzle. Since the criterion for the *Times* and other quality puzzle publications is not to use too many common letters like E, R, and S, Kurzban likes to use "at least one of every letter in each puzzle." While this isn't always possible with letters like Q and Z, he feels that "it's a nice touch for the solver."

Solvers who've never tried a diagramless are in for a delightful and distinctive solving experience when they tackle a Kurzban.

DIAGRAMLESS by Stan Kurzban

(SEE PAGE 263 FOR SOLUTION)

ACROSS

1 Meat of a sort
5 Beast of burden
8 Essayist
9 Gal of song
10 See 29 Across
12 Chessmen: abbr.
13 Bring to bear
14 However
15 Famous fictional cat
16 Shot for Lendl
18 The air: abbr.
19 Send out
21 Tennis unit
23 Abominable snowman
24 State bordering on 58 Down: abbr.
26 —— Bluff, city in 58 Down
27 Serving plate
29 Followed by 10 Across, city in 58 Down
31 Fish —— bait
33 Ignited
35 One who had an Irish Rose
37 With 40 Across, city in 58 Down
40 See 37 Across
42 Preceded by 29 Across, city in 58 Down
44 English river
46 Sunset ——
49 Beast of burden
51 Type of down
53 Type of pit in La Brea
55 —— Barbara
57 Twitch
59 Sandy tract
61 Type: abbr.
63 Preceded by 38 Down, city in 58 Down
66 Hockey superstar Bobby
67 What some animals chew
69 —— Vegas
70 *Inter* ——
72 Having small depressions
74 Dutch commune
75 Self
76 Tyrannosaurus ——
77 Egg drink

DOWN

1 City in 58 Down
2 Natural rubbery substance
3 German article
4 Was in opposition to
5 Agrees
6 City in 58 Down
7 Ai, for example
10 Fish ——
11 African plant
17 Nibbles
20 Type of basin
22 Geog. area
25 Cow, in 73 Down
28 —— City, city in 58 Down
30 Nibble
32 Poetic contraction
34 —— Mahal
36 Summer in Lyons
38 See 63 Across
39 Bone: combining form
41 Prefix for gen or moron
43 Goddess of discord
45 Consume
47 Western st.
48 Hang
50 Krazy ——
52 U. S. —— 101 in 58 Down
54 City in 58 Down
56 Preceded by 55 Across, city in 58 Down
58 A state: abbr.
60 Chemical compound
62 Summarize
64 Road-building machine
65 Dour
68 Preceded by 29 Across, city in 58 Down
71 "I wouldn't send —— on a night like this."
73 Land bordering 58 Down: abbr.

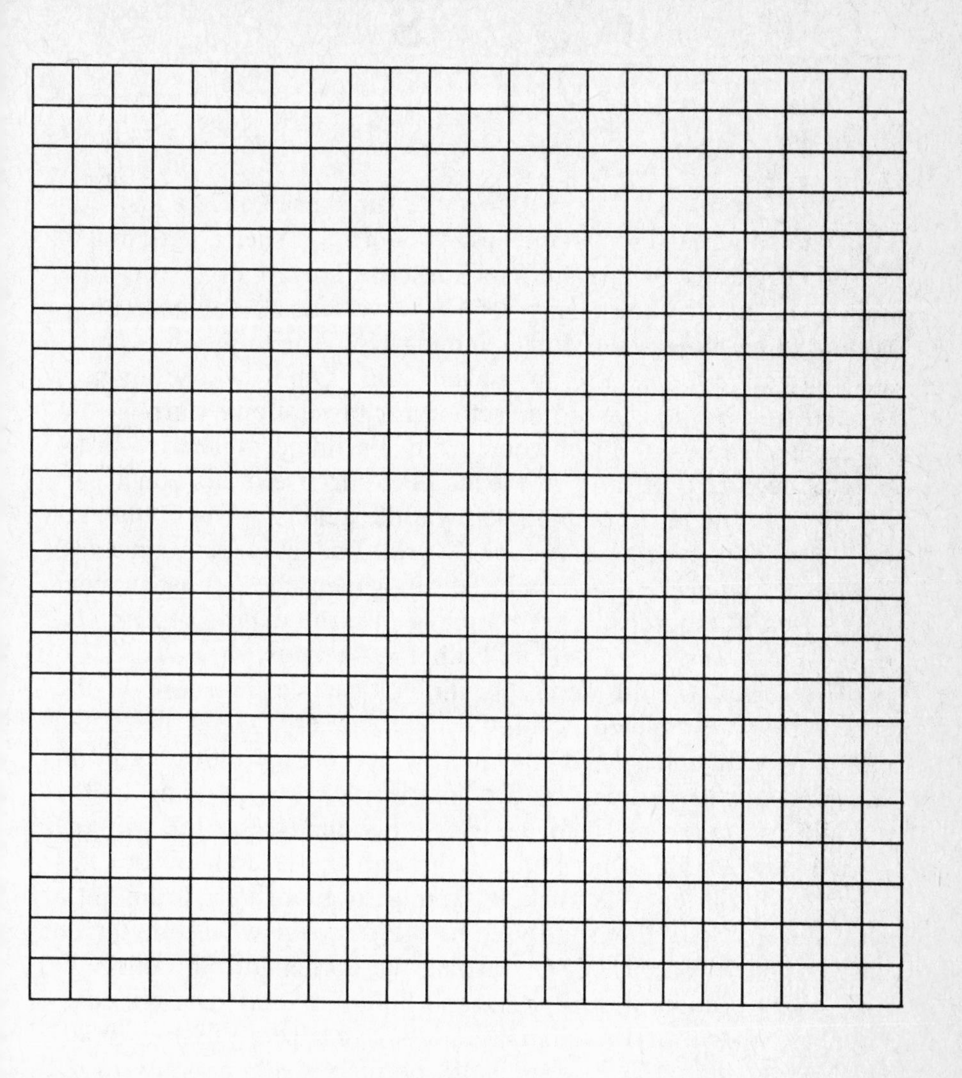

JORDAN LASHER

JORDAN LASHER SPENT the summer of 1978 constructing "the toughest crossword puzzle ever." Lasher's assignment was to create a puzzle that couldn't be solved in twenty-four hours—no matter how many reference volumes a solver had access to. The project was for Hemming-Hulbert Booksellers, Inc., an innovative bookstore in Beachwood, Ohio, whose owners wanted to use a crossword marathon for promotional purposes.

Lasher came to Beachwood from his home in nearby Pittsburgh and carted off fifty reference books to use in his constructing. Sources included cookbooks, wildlife guides, trivia books, art books, a Tolkien glossary, rock 'n' roll encyclopedias, and *The Chemical Engineer's Handbook*. To supplement these, Lasher spent hours in a Pittsburgh library plunging into the depths of *The Oxford English Dictionary* and still other references.

The result was an incredibly difficult puzzle that none of the 186 entrants completed correctly. The winner, *Games* magazine editor Mike Donner, had the highest percentage (88) of correct answers and earned $1,000 for his efforts. He had gone to the marathon as a journalist for *Games* and wound up as the winner.

Donner described his journey through the reference books as a surreal experience. "Imagine having to choose from among a bookstore's thirty thousand volumes to discover where any given answer word was buried. Or turning the corner into the dimly lit mythology section at three A.M. and finding a total stranger cussing about the same Babylonian goddess you were cussing about. Or driving, catatonic, five miles to the nearest library only to realize you'd left your puzzle at the bookstore. Or wondering why you were doing this, or indeed what you were doing, or whether you were doing anything at all."

Examples of the clues include the following generally unknown bits of information:

Postulated feature of the Mare Acidalium	Canal

Luzon municipality	Daet
E.R.A. leader in N.L.: 1921	Doak
Japanese salad of vegetables and fish	Sunomono

Only thirty-two of the original contestants felt confident enough to hand in their puzzles. One contestant, being interviewed on television and informed that Lasher was in a nearby restaurant, wished him ptomaine poisoning.

Lasher himself made two television appearances, spoke on two radio talk shows, and was the subject of a full-page spread in a Pittsburgh newspaper.

Buoyed by this publicity and the overall success of the first marathon, the bookstore commissioned Lasher to create a second "25×25 monster" in 1979. His "Lasher's Thrasher" crossword was difficult, though nowhere near the level of the previous marathon puzzle. The winner was another *Games* editor, Will Shortz, who completed the puzzle in nine hours and thirty minutes and made only three errors. Shortz recalled his state of mind when he handed in his puzzle: "By the time I finished my puzzle at five-thirty Saturday morning, I had just enough energy left to walk to my hotel room and collapse into bed. Other solvers stayed up the full twenty-four hours."

Lasher's clues for the second marathon were based more on trivial information than obscure data:

—— Park, N.Y. 11374	Rego
Howdy Doody's friend	Bob
Player under Jerry Claiborne	Terp
First word in a Paine quote	These

Neither of these puzzles is typical of Lasher's style. For he is identified with creative themes, witty clues, wild wordplay, gimmicky tricks, and much fun.

Lasher's puzzle for the 1979 Stamford Marriott contest was a remarkable *tour de force* based on its title, "Phonetics." Shortz, the tournament director, gave solvers a hint with the blurb "4-warned is 4-armed"—Lasher replaced words with numerals and individual letters in clues like these:

Famous Robert Browning line	O 2 B in England
Estimate by inspection	I ball
Prudent proverb	Look B 4 U leap

Lasher's involvement in puzzles began when he was ten years old and formed a puzzle "partnership" with his father. The two would solve puzzles together as they rode on the NYC subways.

He made his constructing debut a few years later in junior high. Lasher, working on the school newspaper, switched from reporting to constructing when a new feature was needed. He can't remember any of his first clues, but does recall that he misspelled "tomatos" in the diagram. Trying to broaden his horizons, he mailed off a 13×13 to the *New York Post*. What he got back was a form letter saying they purchased crosswords from a syndicate.

Lasher didn't pursue crosswords again until he was a sophomore in college. This time his target was the *Times*. He sent Margaret Farrar "a 15×15 crossword puzzle on a 3×3-inch piece of quadrille paper, with no definitions." Farrar, of course, rejected the puzzle, but encouraged Lasher to read the rules for submitting puzzles and to try again. He did, but was rejected again and forgot about crosswords for seven more years.

In late 1969 Lasher came down with mononucleosis. He had just moved to Pittsburgh, but knew no one there, and returned to his mother's house in the Bronx to recuperate. While there he dug up his old crossword memorabilia. It took about a week to make the needed repairs on the puzzle previously submitted to—and rejected by—Margaret Farrar. Lasher submitted in to Will Weng at the *Times* who accepted it.

From that point on, Lasher's career took off. He found a marvelous mentor in Farrar, who directed him to new markets and bought his puzzles for all her outlets—the Simon & Schuster books and calendars, the Pocket Book series, and the *L.A. Times* Syndicate. Farrar was eventually so fond of him that she flew out to Cleveland as a celebrity guest for the first puzzle marathon. She was eighty-one at the time.

Lasher's themes cover a wide spectrum of topics. He keeps track of new ideas by jotting them down on scratch paper and putting them in his wallet. He constructs mainly 21×21 crosswords, which take him anywhere from eight to ten hours to do. He finds that the definitions are very time-consuming for he strives for originality and takes great pride in not taking any shortcuts—he has never used the same diagram twice.

In "Lack of Composure" Lasher's punny entries were based on composers' names:

Composer's cache	Haydn place
Gift for a composer	Bach scratcher
Words from a picture-taking composer	Watch the Verdi
Some of a composer's music	Handel bars
Novel about composer's fruit	A Gluckwork Orange

In "Definitions" all the themed words were written as "definition of . . ." and included the following clues and entries:

Racehorse	Oatsmobile
Golden Gate Bridge	The car spangled banner
Double-decker bed	A lot of bunk
Double stitch	A sew and sew
Grand Canyon	Hole of fame
IOU	A paper wait
Dark Ages	Knight time
Standing ovation	Applause that refreshes
Dog kennel	Barking lot

Lasher used outrageous riddles in "Riddle, Riddle":

"How did the big mountain know that the little mountain was fibbing?" "It was only a bluff."

"What is worse than raining cats and dogs?" "Hailing taxis."

"What sits on the bottom of the sea and shakes?" "A nervous wreck."

"Why did the pelican eat so many fish?" "To fill the bill."

"What is green and pecks on trees?" "Woody wood pickle."

For "Escape from Reality" Lasher collected a bunch of fakes:

Handbag stuff	Imitation leather
Playing surface	Artificial turf
Carroll reptile	The mock turtle
Would-be systems of knowledge	Pseudo sciences
Computer component	Voice synthesizer
Some choppers	False teeth

In "Anagrams" Lasher clued familiar phrases with their anagrams:

NO WIRE UNSENT	Western Union
HERE COME DOTS	The Morse Code
I RULE FINANCES	Life insurance
ACTOR INDEED	Eddie Cantor
A FLARING END	Grand finale
GRAND OLD EVILS	Gold and silver

In "Turn of Phrase" Lasher juxtaposed common expressions:

Shuts off a tape recorder	Presses the stop
Is doomed to eternal cachinnation	Laughs for good
Heroic wild dog?	Jackal of the day
Statistician's dissertation	Speech of figures
Destroys Boulder secretly	Torpedoes the dam

Lasher's original clues include:

Prepare to feather	Tar
Meet me —— Louis	Inst.
Saves nine	Sews
Yoko's cry?	Ono

Lasher co-authored the *Crossword Puzzle Compendium,* a book about the crossword world and the people in it. He also created the Sunday crosswords for *The Boston Globe* for three years, alternating with Emily Cox and Henry Rathvon. His puzzles were so popular that solvers formed a Lasher fan club.

Lasher, a tall and handsome man in his mid-thirties, has a "real" career as an executive for an oil company. The California-based Lasher found that his job, extensive travels, and crossword commitment left him with almost no time to spend with his wife and two children. Every other weekend he would lock himself up in his study and work on his crosswords. So he reluctantly resigned his position with *The Boston Globe* in 1986.

Lasher, like many of the other constructors profiled here, has seen many changes in crosswords since he started constructing.

He feels that the markets for constructors have expanded tremendously, new-wave clues are impacting on crosswords, and crossword solvers are more tolerant of new ideas, themes, and clues. In short, Lasher sees crosswords in a positive way—just the way solvers view him and his puzzles.

TEAMWORK by Jordon Lasher

(SEE PAGE 263 FOR SOLUTION)

ACROSS

1 Beat it!
5 Northern abodes
11 Be a ham
14 Hair style
18 Contempoary actor + famous clergyman
20 Pedro's emphatic affirmative
21 Event for teen-agers
22 Gypsy + McRae + Myron + Octavus Roy
24 One of the Bears
25 Malay dagger
26 Barnyard sound
27 Movie rat
28 Star of "Route 66"
30 Kind of sack
31 Table scrap
33 Reverential
35 Oil grp.
36 Church sight
38 Fine-tuned
41 Heating medium
44 Heavenly body
47 Suffers
49 Bake eggs
50 Expunge
51 Singer Rawls
52 Baby she-bears: Lat.
54 Kind of sack
56 Author Bagnold *(National Velvet)*
57 Patty Duke ——
59 Song refrain
60 Verb ending
61 Icelandic epic
62 *War and Peace* heroine
64 Coloring
66 So long!
68 "Volare (—— Blu, Dipinto Blu)"
69 City on the Allegheny
70 "The —— near"
72 Where Hercules slew the lion
74 Grain bristle
76 Teaching degs.
78 Diminutive suffix
79 Emulate Dr. J
82 Back talk
84 He raised Cain
86 —— *the Worlds*
88 Boy's nickname
89 Fastener
90 Actress Garr
91 Bill
93 Hwy.
94 Meara and Murray
96 Posed again
98 Table spread
99 Call for help
100 Woman of the house
101 Almost at
103 Thomas —— Edison
105 City near Anaheim
107 Units of 256 pounds, in old England
108 GOP opponent
109 Core
112 Enemies, literary style
114 Answer to 26 Across?
115 Possessed
118 Italian cheese
120 Jai ——
121 Beatle's family + actress' family
125 Norse goddess of spring
126 Jejune
127 *Rocky III* star + *Airport '77* star
128 For fear that
129 Wriggler
130 Famous admiral
131 Stable staple

DOWN

1 Local humane orgs.
2 *Do I —— Waltz?*
3 "No Right Turn ——"
4 "Don't Tread ——"
5 Where the cochlea is
6 Merchandise: abbr.
7 Novelist O'Flaherty
8 —— account (never)
9 Group of eight
10 Jiff
11 Appearance
12 Svc. branch
13 *Gremlins* pet
14 It shaded Isaac Newton
15 Nobel novelist + Gom[e]r Pyle
16 Clothesline
17 The Tentmaker
19 Children's moralist?
20 Built with open sides
23 Witch doctor's practice
29 —— *dixit*
32 Literary waif + actor
34 *West Side Story* director + country singer
37 Musical mark
39 Painter Max
40 Vamp + flying nun
42 Stage whisper
43 Olympics reward
44 *Good Earth* heroine
45 Santa ——
46 Comedian + Bridges + Brummell
48 Roofing material
52 Turn away from
53 Dress style
55 One of the Pipers
58 Suffix with different

63 Fought
65 US missile
67 ". . . is as good as ——"
71 Control system, for short
73 Nigerian native
74 State of India
75 "I —— Be Loved"
77 Garment for a ranee
80 Mother of Zeus
81 Windows to the soul
83 Candy flavor
85 Give an Oscar for a TV show
87 Alley Oop's girlfriend
92 In cloak-and-dagger style
95 *Peter Pan* pirate
97 Toward the back
102 City near Toronto
104 Love, Italian style
106 Vase handles
109 Blood: comb. form
110 Transplant, in a way
111 Petty officers
112 Disappoint
113 Kind of shoppe
114 Court payment
116 Indigo
117 Insecticides
119 Office letter
122 *Uno, due,* ——
123 Part of SC or SD: abbr.
124 That girl

WILLIAM LUTWINIAK

ALTHOUGH RECORDS aren't kept in such matters, William Lutwiniak is probably the most prolific constructor in this or any other country in the world. It's almost impossible to find an editor of mass-market puzzle magazines or syndicated puzzles who doesn't depend on a batch of Lutwiniak puzzles to meet deadlines.

Lutwiniak has constructed more than 6,500 crosswords ranging in size from 13 × 13 to 23 × 23. Defining himself as a "craftsman," he can turn out a small puzzle in fifteen minutes and a larger one in an hour. However, he can also work for four to six hours on special crosswords.

His puzzles are almost always themed and cover every topic imaginable. Examples:

Philadelphia—Seventy-sixers, Brotherly love, Mummers' parade
Top people—president, commander, numero uno, director
Reproductions—facsimile, photostat, lookalike, duplicate
Playing cards—jackanapes, ace of clubs, kingfisher, Queensland

Solving puzzles has been an integral part of Lutwiniak's personal and professional life since childhood. As a youth he perfected his solving skills on the cryptograms in *Detective Fiction Weekly*. After winning a solving contest from that magazine with its prize of a free subscription to *The Cryptogram,* published by the American Cryptogram Association, he learned how to construct cryptograms. Then he joined the National Puzzlers' League and its offshoot, The New York Riddlers.

Taking his solving and constructing skills a step further than most people, he joined the Signal Intelligence Service, precursor of the National Security Agency (NSA), and worked his way up through the ranks to the position of senior cryptologist.

Cryptograms are regular features in thousands of newspapers and appear in most of the mass-market puzzle magazines. Variations include "Dial-A-Word" or "Phone Talk" columns that use the numerals found on telephones to code sayings, quotes, or proverbs. In this type of puzzle "2" can stand for "A," "B," or "C"; "3" can stand for "D," "E," or "F." Examples follow (answers are on page 99):

36657 7874 46 94373 264357 3327 86 87323.

663 4663 8876 33737837 2668437.

Lutwiniak's first crosswords were published in *The New York Herald Tribune* when he was only fourteen. Concentrating on his career as a professional cryptologist, he solved crosswords during his lunch breaks and constructed them after working hours. He divided the puzzle-making process into categories—definitions, grids, themes, etc.—and worked on one aspect at a time. As he recalls, "this enabled me to do something every evening, no matter how little time I had. If I had only a half hour, I could type up defs for that long. If I had an hour, I could define a big crossword."

Now retired, Lutwiniak no longer needs his assembly-line method but follows the construction process through from beginning to end. His wife is an active assistant—drawing the grids, checking and typing the definitions. In return, Lutwiniak publishes some of his puzzles under her maiden name, Jeanne Newland.

With his white hair and tall stature Lutwiniak looks like an elder statesman. He's quite distinguished-looking and very soft-spoken.

Lutwiniak's small puzzles can be solved fairly rapidly for he feels that daily solvers work the puzzles in a limited time situation and just want a "quick fix." But for Sunday crosswords and those in specialized magazines, Lutwiniak believes the solver expects a workout. Two of his classic crosswords were "Spot Announcements" and "Reading Letters," both published in the *Times*

"Spot Announcements" contained rebus-style clues such as AC, WHE, NE, and HE, which were the literal definitions of their answers—"center of attraction," "the middle of nowhere," "end of the line," and "top of the heap."

Some solvers didn't understand the gimmick even after the solution was subsequently printed. W. A. Morgan wrote a letter to the *Times* protesting that editor Will Weng threw solvers "a real curve ball" and demanding to know the meanings of "all those apparently meaningless initials."

In his explanatory letter Will Weng wrote, "The letter clues were supposed to give the literal definitions of the complete answer. Thus the clue WHE yielded the answer 'The middle of nowhere,' and the middle letters of the word 'nowhere' are WHE.''

''Reading Letters'' was similarly oriented:

H	Beethoven's fifth
AF	Half a loaf
Of of of of of of of of of of	Oftentimes
A	First of all
CCCCCCC	Seven seas
H	Quarter of an hour
O	Second in command
Y	The fourth of July

Lutwiniak's terse cluing is reminiscent of some of the classic enigmas based on letters of the alphabet. The following is answered by the letter ''E'':

The beginning of eternity;
The end of time and space;
The beginning of every end,
And the end of every place.

Lutwiniak must have used his NSA training for two really tricky puzzles, ''Invisibility'' and ''Do-It-Yourself,'' which could probably qualify as NSA employment tests. ''Invisibility'' contained eight blank spaces in the clue list, which were answered by the following—''gone with the wind,'' ''not present,'' ''blank space,'' ''out of sight,'' ''in absentia,'' ''among the missing,'' ''disappearing act,'' and ''nowhere to be seen.''

''Do-It-Yourself'' contained nine unclued numbers and one clue indicated only with an asterisk. The unclued numbers yielded ''without a clue,'' ''uninformative,'' ''missing link,'' ''meaningless,'' ''drawing a blank,'' ''ill defined,'' ''nothing at all,'' ''wide open spaces'' and ''without meaning.'' The asterisk clue yielded ''unnumbered.'' Several solvers wrote to Will Weng complaining about sloppy proofreading. But the majority of solvers appreciated the gimmick and clamored for more.

Lutwiniak's easy puzzles require no reference books, but his more difficult ones can rack the brain. For Baltimore's First Annual Crossword Open Lutwiniak constructed a crossword around a quote from then Attorney General Ramsey Clark—''There is no conflict between liberty and safety. We will have both or neither." Nonthematic clues included:

Took a spouse	Wived
Unlike some stones?	Mossy
Paperless puppies	Mutts
Diamond home	Plate

Lutwiniak's "Fruit Salad" crossword for the second Ridgewood Newspapers Crossword Tournament was the puzzle that really separated the top contestants from the dilettantes. Clues included:

Peach	A choice example of its kind
Lemon	Washout, failure, dud, or flop
Fig	An all but worthless trifle
Plum	Something fine or superior
Melon	Windfall for stockholders
Date	Engagement or appointment

Lutwiniak is as busy in his retirement as he was when he was working full time for the NSA. He constructs crosswords for most of the mass-market puzzle magazines, the *Times*, the Running Press and Simon & Schuster collections, several syndicates, and such magazines as *Americana*, *Palm Beach Life*, and *Pipeliner's Monthly*. He also designed all the crosswords for Pago Pago, a competitive crossword game for two to four players.

Lutwiniak is able to come up with numerous synonyms for his larger themed puzzles. In his "Grapevine" crossword he clued gossip(s) with the following—common talk, busybodies, tattletales, rumormonger, noises about, muckrakers, chatterbox, dish the dirt, and scuttlebutt. In a "Lutwiniak" crossword, solvers could use these entries—prolific, analytical, able, erudite, intelligent, clever, amusing, terrific!

ANSWERS—LUTWINIAK

Dial-A-Word

1. Fools rush in where angels fear to tread.
2. One good turn deserves another.

TAKING NOTE by William Lutwiniak

(SEE PAGE 264 FOR SOLUTION)

ACROSS

1 Gram. abbr.
5 St. sign
8 *The —— Quartet*
11 Sub's ears
16 Proceedings
17 Ottoman's kin
19 Unassisted
20 —— *Real*
21
24 Things to do
25 Diaskeuast
26
28 Island east of Tonga
29 Sea off Greece: var.
30 "Once —— time . . ."
31 Put up money
33 Beverage ending
34 Pancake
35 Do battle
38
43 Have —— (be wary)
45 Grid prop
46 Off one's feed
47 Running account
48 Instructs
49 Goes by
52 Henry —— Wallace
53 Like some eyes
54 Miss Jeanmaire
55 One of the Waughs
56 Detours
57
62 Of a main road
65 Polar sea
66 Norse pantheon
70 Most orderly
71 Very apt
73 Luck
75 Cylindrical
76 Tumulus
77 Relation
78 TV's Dawber
79 Margin of victory
80
84 Poetic word
85 Be an angel
86 A crowd, in Cremona
87 Sachet scent
88 Yahoo
90 Uighur, e.g.
93 Ending with phlegm
94
98 Of six
101 Missouri feeder
102
104 Roughed it
105 Amor's wings
106 Chromosome unit
107 Actor Richard ——
108 Dionysian reveler
109 Neighbor of Isr.
110 Patriotic org.
111 Fasces makeup

DOWN

1 Kitchen spice
2 Part of AMPAS
3 Skinny galoot
4 He discovered the St. Lawrence
5 Ascus member
6 First lady, before Eleanor
7 Win a bike race
8 Burt Ward role
9 Ma Bell's boy
10 With elation
11 Author Françoise ——
12 End of a series
13 Caravel of 1492
14 ". . . —— wore a red red rose"
15 Certain horse
18 Overlook
19 Lobby item
20 *Lili* star
22 "—— the Top"
23 Female sandpiper
27 Ron Howard role
31 Type of fall
32 Poplar
33 Catches something
34 Auk or hawk
35 Belt site
36 Water buffalo
37 Timeouts
39 Struggle
40 Perimeter
41 Changes over time
42 Blemish
43 Like a small hollow
44 Juliet was one
48 Trillion: prefix
50 Leon small change
51 Hide
52 "The Louisville Lip"
53 Syn., often
55 Part of NATO
56 Amtrak and Pennsy
58 Seine feeder
59 Do handwork
60 Cheese dish
61 Ending with verb
62 Square columns
63 What alums do
64 Fife player's drum
67 Shipowner's man on

board
68 Lake of Finland
69 Joel Chandler Harris character
71 Kin to mere
72 Miss McClanahan
73 Bona ——
74 Hush-hush Nav. org.
76 Los Pirineos
77 Like certain ears
80 Maudlin sentimentality
81 "Hogan's Heroes" locale
82 In the public eye
83 Ben Franklin, once
85 Stood up to
88 Miss Comden
89 Sign up
90 Embattled
91 —— up (eye)
92 Chill
93 Played Lou Grant
94 Some condos
95 Kind of market
96 Wild declamation
97 Put trust in
99 Interpreted
100 Cravings
103 Miss Alicia

EUGENE T. MALESKA

EUGENE MALESKA, present editor of the *New York Times* crosswords, is fascinated with letter patterns in words. When he met Don Rubin, creator of a nationally syndicated visual-puzzle column, the first thing Maleska remarked on was the other man's name. "Don Rubin," he mused, "consonant, vowel, consonant, consonant, vowel. . . ." Maleska's concern with letter patterns befits a person who edits more than forty thousand clues a year.

Maleska estimates that more than one million people work the *Times* crossword every day. In addition, the *Times* puzzles are reprinted in one hundred other newspapers for millions of additional solvers to tackle. The impact of these numbers is not lost on Maleska. He works seven days a week to maintain the high *Times* standards set up by his predecessors Farrar and Weng, while simultaneously stamping the crosswords with his own imprint.

Maleska believes that "a crossword is an entertainment, but it should have some uplifting and educational value. The first thing for me is to make it a pleasure; but I also try to make it a challenge."

This philosophy reflects his impressive educational credentials—a bachelor's degree in Latin, a master's degree in English literature, both from Montclair State College, and a doctorate from Harvard. A former teacher who became a superintendent of schools in New York City, he left the school system in 1977 to assume his editorial position at the *Times*.

Maleska started to solve crosswords as a teenager when he found a discarded newspaper on the subway and discovered the crossword page. He became an expert solver in college. When he met his future bride, Jean, who shared his passion for Latin and crosswords, he courted her with original puzzles. The first one contained the clue "Most beautiful girl on campus" for "Jean."

Jean's roommate, a go-getter type, told her, "Your boyfriend can make money with his puzzles. The *Herald Tribune* pays five dollars for those in the daily papers." Jean encouraged Maleska to set about getting published.

This was no simple task. Maleska remembers the route he traveled: "First I bought the newspaper every day and studied the style of the puzzle very carefully. Months later I submitted my first professional effort—and held my breath. I had enclosed a self-addressed stamped envelope, but did not bother to write an accompanying letter. I had too much *amour propre* to plead. My bubble of self-esteem burst abruptly. Not even a formal rejection slip! I was tempted to give up right then and there. But persistence emerged to take the place of pride. . . . I set some sort of record for initial failure—over forty rejections from a silent editor in a two-year period!"

By the time Maleska's first puzzle was published he and Jean were married. They were driving along a street near their home when Jean opened the newspaper and whooped triumphantly, "Your puzzle is here in the paper!" Maleska was so nervous that he almost drove the car off the road.

Maleska soon started to sell most of his puzzles and supplemented his teaching salary by constructing crosswords. He became a regular contributor to the *Herald Tribune*. One day he asked the new editor if she would permit him to jazz up the clues and she agreed.

He vividly remembers the first puzzle in which he "broke the log jam." " 'Nest' was defined as 'Nutcracker's suite' and the clue for 'noon' was 'When both hands are up.' For 'ironer' the solvers were confronted with 'He has pressing problems.' "

"Well, the fan mail was wonderful! Out of the woods came scores of people who cried for more. Constructors were encouraged to use other original clues in various places throughout their puzzles."

When Maleska expanded his markets and started submitting puzzles to Margaret Farrar at the *Times* he persuaded her to use multiple word entries, the first of which was "hard-shell crab." In the beginning, Farrar always indicated the number of words in the answer, but after a while she said to Maleska, "Why should we baby these folks?," and stopped marking the definitions with "two words," "three words," etc.

Maleska found Farrar to be very receptive to new ideas. In 1964 she published his first "Stepquote," a crossword whose answer is a quote that descends through the diagram from the upper left to the lower right corners.

The reaction from fans was overwhelming. Those who praised

the idea compared the Stepquote to an acrostic "because the unkeyed letters at the crossings of the angles required them to use brainpower to fill in the missing letters." However, others were frustrated in their solving efforts and complained that they couldn't find "Stepquote" in their dictionaries. The *Times* devoted an entire "Letters to the Editor" column to comments about the Stepquote.

Through the years Maleska improved on his original Stepquote by cutting down the unkeyed areas to almost half. The puzzle has become a regular feature in book collections and the *Times* puzzle page.

Maleska's puzzle work is all-consuming. In addition to his work for the *Times* he has edited seventeen *Crossword Books of Quotations* and three books of cryptic crosswords for Simon & Schuster. He became Farrar's co-editor on the S & S crossword books in 1978; after her death he hired John Samson to assist him. Maleska has written two books, *A Pleasure in Words* and *Across and Down,* and also constructs crosswords for Dell Publishing Company.

Dell publishes more than 120 different issues of mass-market puzzle magazines per year. Editor in chief Rosalind Moore directs a staff of more than twenty editors and free-lancers to maintain the high standards set up by her predecessor, Kathleen Rafferty. Moore's favorite constructor is Maleska, whose work appears regularly in Dell's magazines.

An avid solver herself, Moore often tackles the *Times* puzzle in the evening before going to bed. On May 28, 1982, she was overjoyed to discover that the daily puzzle was a public birthday card to her from Maleska. The two entries on the top horizontal row were defined as "Actress Russell" ("Rosalind") and "Part of MTM" ("Moore") while the two corresponding entries on the bottom horizontal row were clued as "One of a tiny septet" ("Happy") and "Arrival time" ("Birthday"). Moore was so excited when she finished solving the puzzle that she called Maleska at home late in the evening and woke him up to thank him.

Maleska works out of his house, "Over Jordan," in Cape Cod, Massachusetts. His study is filled with reference works which include four complete sets of encyclopedias as well as several unabridged dictionaries. He keeps notebooks of all of his definitions, filed by word length. He methodically codes each clue with a "T" when he uses it in the *Times*. Before her death in 1983, Jean Maleska was her husband's very able assistant. She fact checked clues, test-solved the puzzles, typed his correspondence, and accompanied him to puzzle get-togethers.

Although Maleska put his own mark on the crosswords, he followed Weng's advice about making the daily puzzles more difficult as the week progresses. "Will Weng suggested that I start off with easy ones on Monday. For a solver to be hit with a hard puzzle on Monday would be too much."

By looking at a selected week of Maleska's clues it's possible to see how he varies the puzzle from day to day. During the week of April 14 to 19, 1986, the following puzzles appeared:

Monday—easy theme, easy definitions and easy entries:

Surpass easily	Run rings around
Be feverish	Run a temperature
Is a family trait	Runs in the blood

Tuesday—the theme was still easy; this time it was words with "head" in them—"Brideshead" ("Waugh setting"); "Headline" ("Streamer, e.g."); "Headwind" ("Sailor's problem"). There were a few punny clues:

The world according to Arp	Monde
Flattered sincerely?	Imitated
The buck starts here	Mint

Wednesday—Maleska used a geographical theme with entries like "Lake Tanganyika," "Yellowstone Lake," and "Antarctic Ocean."

Thursday's theme was more abstract and was based on different pronunciations of "ough." Themed words included *"Once Is Not Enough,"* "Plough through," "Cough medicine," and "Glazed doughnuts" (clued as "They surround some holes"). Also, some of the clues were a little unexpected—"Buck's tail?" for "Aroo," and "Where success comes before work: Abbr." for "Dict."

Friday was a punny day with an indication that the four themed clues were "pointed puns." These were:

Coniferous vista	Pines and needles
Hoarding carpet layer	Tacks collector

Cobbler's heirloom	Awl in the family
Truncate not your queries!	Ax me no questions

On Saturday Maleska clued common words with less recognizable definitions:

Sontags	Capes
Obloquy	Abuse
Menhaden's cousin	Shad
Tantara	Blare

Maleska devotes one day a week to answering letters. Because of the stature of the *Times* puzzle, Maleska receives thousands of letters a year from solvers he classifies into four groups:

Sleepers—those who accept whatever comes along. Sleepers see crossword editors and constructors as all-knowing demigods who make no mistakes. Their letters are usually the "keep up the good work" type.

Squawkers—serious solvers whose egos are bruised when they can't finish a puzzle. They write nasty letters to the editor threatening to cancel their subscriptions or organize a solvers' strike.

Leapers—impulsive solvers who rush in with criticisms over alleged errors without first checking all the facts.

Gotchas—in Maleska's words, "a mixture of cool customers who know their onions, their literature, movies, geography, foreign languages, sports, music, and other fields in which I occasionally reveal my humanity by making an error."

In *Across and Down* Maleska chronicled some of the flubs he made during his career. Most of these occur in the definitions, for example, defining Abba Eban as the "first Israeli ambassador to the U.S." when Ambassador Elath deserved that distinction. When Maleska relied on his memory for sports clues, he mistakenly called Terry Bradshaw "Bradford," made Larry Bird a relative of Admiral Byrd, and confused golfer Ed Sneed with Sam and J. C. Snead.

Times crossword solvers are quick to respond to novel puzzles. When Maleska published Ronald Friedman's "Strip Tees" puzzle in 1979, he received a flood of mail. The gimmick Friedman used was to remove every "T" from the answers. Thus, "Tim's tune" became "Ipoe hrough he ulips" ("Tiptoe through the tulips") and "Nondrinker" was answered by "Eeoaler"

(''Teetotaler''). The *Times* published David Galef's letter, which was written in the same style: Galef found this puzzle ''quie a surprise'' and presumed ''i joled a lo of he fans ou of heir rouine.''

Maleska feels there are mixed reactions to Stepquotes, verses, doggerel, rebus, and gimmicky puzzles and he likes to mix them up. ''Discretion dictates that such creations be published now and then as a change of pace.'' One time, after he had published three verse puzzles on three successive Sundays, he got lots of complaints, including his favorite: ''Your puzzles are getting verse and verse.''

Maleska knows that ''a crossword puzzle editor cannot please all of the people all of the time.'' On one day he received two very different letters from solvers—one complaining that the puzzles were too hard and threatening to organize a solvers' strike, and the other complaining that the puzzles were ''ridiculously easy.'' Maleska removed the names and addresses from both letters and sent each solver the other's lament. He never heard from either one again.

When Will Weng passed the editorial reins over to Maleska he said, ''Crosswords are only a pastime, but you are about to discover how many thousands of people take them so seriously that you would think they're a matter of life and death.''

Maleska rapidly learned how important the *Times* puzzle is to millions of people. And while he finds out immediately if he's made a mistake, he points out that ''very few missiles are aimed'' at him in their missives. He believes that ''if all members of the human race were as nice as crossword fans, this would be a far better world.''

STEPQUOTE by Eugene T. Maleska

(SEE PAGE 264 FOR SOLUTION)

ACROSS

1 Start of the Stepquote
7 First name of 45 Across
13 Event on the Charles
20 Pungent snuff
21 Plunder
22 One ——
23 Creator of the Kewpie
24 Disinclined
25 Brisk rides
26 Amin of Uganda
27 Rural sight
29 Gibe
31 Word with part or plate
32 Face: Spanish
34 Sparkle
35 Spinner in space
37 Game for two
38 Winged
39 C-notes
40 Purpose of a hansa
41 Cave-dwelling scavenger
43 Extinguish
45 Stepquote author
46 Ingredient of some soaps
47 Dutch genre painter, 17th century
49 Word used with Alaska
50 One having taking ways
51 Singer Ray
53 Committed perjury
54 Dweller in Asgard
55 High neon letters in NYC
58 Most balanced
59 Myrmecologist's topic
60 Olivier's title
61 Wild duck
62 Charter
63 Third part of the Stepquote
67 Find distasteful
68 Elevator magnate
69 DDE
70 Onetime post of 69 Across
71 Truman's Secretary of State
73 Part of a journey
74 King Cotton's bundle
76 Flip the pages
77 "—— is on me"
78 Handel's birthplace
80 Labor leader
81 Contralto Nikolaidi
82 Ingenious
84 Tall and thin
85 Italian staple
87 *Beau* ——
88 Birchbark
89 Last Judgment
90 Cacholong
94 Freudian topic
95 Speaker like Cicero
97 John Ridd's bride
98 In the bow
99 Bridle hand
101 Hebrew letter
102 Satisfied
104 Italian pronoun
105 As a whole
107 Hawaiian's sweetheart
109 Engage
111 Workman who shaves blemishes from leather
112 Worshipful one
113 Baleful phrase
114 Resonance
115 Shell group
116 End of the Stepquote

DOWN

1 Beethoven's Third
2 Wanton defacer
3 Garden spider
4 Inst. at Troy, N.Y.
5 Hound's sound
6 Second part of the Stepquote
7 Point in the outer ear
8 Ports of a sort
9 Out in the open
10 Like swamplands
11 Kiang
12 Pony or sheepdog
13 Author of *Phèdre*
14 Growing out
15 Ending for nona, deca, etc.
16 Memo abbr.
17 Work by 45 Across
18 Ends
19 Storehouse
28 Incandescence
30 Ford
33 Battle of the Bulge loca
35 Snooped
36 Possessive pronoun
40 Rank first
42 One, in Edinburgh
44 Gallic name
45 Emulate Chagall
46 Hanoi's Le Duc——
47 Dike rock
48 Source of the Stepquote
49 Toledo product
50 Ominous indication
51 City in NE China
52 Prima ballerina
54 Small bird
56 Start of a T. Williams title
57 Coeur d'——, city in Idaho
60 Obdurate
61 —— Galilee
64 About 2.8 lbs. in Greece

65 Nader's *Unsafe —— Speed*

66 Fourth part of the Stepquote

72 Symbol of satiety

74 More melancholy

75 The works

76 Man of La Mancha

79 In the stern

80 Frigate bird

82 Eternal

83 Office of a vicarious ruler

84 Behind schedule

85 Important workers

86 Tops

88 Salad ingredient

89 Pass, peak or lake in Nevada

91 Variety of grapefruit

92 Like an operatic air

93 Inclined

96 German word form with pfeffer or braten

97 French area, rich in coal

100 Turnover

102 G.I. meal

103 Darnel

106 Playwright's favorite letters

108 Blather

110 Thirty-gallon cask

TIMOTHY MARTIN

ROBERT MORLEY CAN'T understand why people solve crosswords. In the introduction to *The Hamlyn Book of Crosswords,* the English actor wrote that there's absolutely no hope for the addicted solver. "You cannot save a man from drowning who refuses to leave the water. As soon as they have solved the puzzle, or finally abandoned the attempt, they crave fresh stimulation. . . . What makes the plight of the crossword puzzlers so pitiable is that there is seldom any monetary award attached."

Morley's tongue-in-cheek introduction is not really far removed from reality. Solvers of cryptic crosswords become addicted to the special solving skills required to crack the coded clues. Constructors of cryptics can also become addicted to the genre. That's what happened to Timothy Martin, one of the newest stars in the cryptic world.

Martin, a systems analyst from Streamwood, Illinois, in "real life," started constructing cryptics in 1981 and sent his first puzzle to *Games* magazine. He remembers how he felt when he received a standard form rejection letter. "In those days I tended to discourage easily and might never have gone on to construct if I hadn't had a second puzzle done. For lack of anything better, I sent it in with a little hope, and lo and behold, some *Games* editor saw potential in what was, in retrospect, a perfectly awful effort."

That editor was Henry Hook (see page 66), master of every type of crossword. He wrote "long, patient letters" to Martin. Later on, two other *Games* editors, Emily Cox and Henry Rathvon (see page 36), continued to encourage Martin and helped him firm up his cryptic clues and enhance his understanding of the process.

These three editors pointed out in a "gentle, encouraging way" where Martin "had violated cryptic clue 'rules.' " Martin notes, "At that time I only understood about thirty percent of what I needed in order to construct cryptics."

Martin was a rapid learner under such expert tutelage and soon saw his first cryptic published in *Games*. He couldn't have been happier, for he had been "convinced that the publication of anything—puzzles, literature, and so forth—depended on knowing an inner circle that was impossible to crack."

Now that he is an established cryptic constructor, Martin's work appears regularly in *Games,* Dell *Champion* publications, and Eugene Maleska's Simon & Schuster books.

Martin's puzzle activities started when he was just five years old, with number and math-oriented puzzles. He progressed to crosswords when he was ten, spending one to two hours on a 15×15 and making extensive use of the *Dell Crossword Dictionary*.

Martin started to solve and construct cryptics at the same time. He learned to solve them through "trial and error and error and error. . . ." His solving time couldn't even be measured in "days, weeks, or eons." Martin "rarely completely solved them" until he "started constructing (oddly enough) and learned more of the ground rules from patient editors."

Martin concentrates mainly on cryptics though he will occasionally construct a standard crossword. His favorite crossword is "Yankee Honorees," a 21×21 published in *Dell Champion Crossword Puzzles*. Martin's reasons for liking this puzzle are related to his love of words. "When I construct standard American crosswords I always use somebody else's grid pattern cribbed from a puzzle magazine—I have a limited visual imagination. One day though, I started fooling with the names of American Nobel literature laureates, and this puzzle resulted. Not only is the grid entirely my own, a minor achievement, but I find the harmony astounding. That 'Nobel Literature Prizes' fits as a twenty-one-letter entry is one thing, but that the names themselves fit so perfectly is something else again. Consider that what—eight? ten?—Americans have won the prize in total. The ease with which the names interlock in the grid is either a startling coincidence or—my preferred explanation—yet another example of the beautiful symmetry of the language."

Martin's entries included Ernest Hemingway, William Faulkner, Sinclair Lewis, John Steinbeck, Saul Bellow, and Pearl S. Buck.

Martin loves to write cryptic clues and enjoys the devious wordplay involved. Asked for his favorite clues, he responded with these examples and added explanations of just why he likes them:

"Jerk to look up Ruth's outfit" = "Yankees"

"This was a Down entry in the diagram. It had just the right touch of bawdiness, and the resolution of 'Ruth's outfit' into 'Yankees' makes for a nice surprise for the solver."

"Wants first part of Steinbeck's *East of Eden* badly" = "Needs"

"A clue like that wouldn't have worked if Hemingway had happened to write *East of Eden.*"

"Underworld skimming top 25% off of Swiss capital tied up in dope" = "Inferno"

"Another Down entry: INF (~~B~~ERN)O. Almost too complex. But just almost."

"Chief of scoundrels, utterly?" = "Head over heels"

"A pun so bad only its creator could love it."

Martin, of course, uses the standard type of wordplay in his cryptics. Here are examples:

Hidden Answers:

Peers inside pearl six-shooter	Earls
Studies extract of serum in a test	Ruminates
Interior of run-down wreck	Undo
Runner, veering, has to shake	Unnerve
Gimlet on ice has mixer in it	Tonic

Containers:

Search in fortunetellers' closets	Se(quest)ers
Black Beauty initially included in markdown	Sa(b)le
Pumpkin sustains fellow glutton	Gour(man)d

Anagrams:

Curious item I made as present	Immediate
Storm caused by racy N.Y. photo	Typhoon

Charades:

Serve up aces with bottom of net crooked	Dish + ones + t
Raise pistol case cover	Up + holster
Expert on eyesight's condition	Pro + vision

Double Definitions:

One who grows pot	Planter
Arguments in lines	Rows

Deletions:

Settlement with no ultimate boundary mark	Colon~~y~~

Homophones:

Storytellers using harps in oral rendition	Liars
Low point for consumer advocate, say	Nadir

Martin is a warm and witty correspondent, but receives no mail from solvers. However, he receives "no death threats either, so it all evens out."

Martin has no time to solve crosswords anymore. "Constructing is just too time-consuming and interesting to leave much time for solving."

However, solvers who crack the cryptic code and become enamored of this genre are only too happy to let Martin and the other cryptic masters continue to construct. Music critic Alan Rich eloquently expressed the appeal of cryptics. He wrote the following about the puzzles from the London *Times* that are reprinted in *New York* magazine, but his words are applicable to all cryptics: "There's a time and place, and a state of mind, for working them. You can stare blankly at a grid for hours, and a little later everything falls into place. These puzzles bug you, the way American puzzles never do."

CRYPTIC CROSSWORD by Timothy Martin

(*SEE PAGE 264 FOR SOLUTION*)

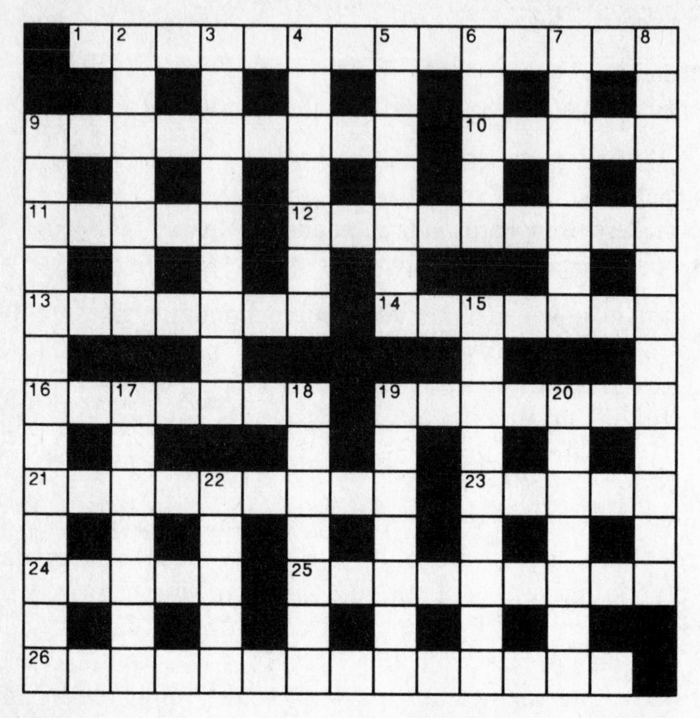

ACROSS

1 Statements made in defense of lunch fees? (14)
9 Cause resistance in Caesar's westward advance (9)
10 Saw wood for strips, backing (5)
11 Verbally criticized a mammal (5)
12 Cardinal sees Latin plays (9)
13 Forces ring Christian's foe, with no right, near outskirts of Ephesus (7)
14 How dog relates to cat in many pounds in New York in the morning (7)
16 One hood from coat with a blank back is what the Poles wear (7)
19 Sailors starting off *Ain't Misbehavin'* refrain (7)
21 Showing desire to obtain one third of photos without a form (9)
23 Opposite from base, besieging troops initially returned for orders (5)
24 Clod gathered from planetoid investigation turned over (5)
25 Willingness to run for sweets, holding a scoundrel back (9)
26 Chemistry, e.g., in foreign mountains between Mr. Turner and fair, playful niece (7, 7)

DOWN

2 Said to be cover for a racket: a possible setup for the numbers? (7)
3 Desire to relive an era that's lost again, sadly! (9)
4 "Cheer up!" according to leader of some people avoiding wedding ceremony (7)
5 Revolutionary leader left main London district (7)
6 Deliberate firing of clergyman without pressure (5)
7 Buggy racing enthralls East European native (7)
8 Giving fellows pitch on the ultimate in army surplus (13)
9 I'm getting hitch securing a teen's van in unplanned delivery (13)
15 Around curve (treacherous), tired vet to take a spin (4, 5)
17 Stogies rolled, not finished on time for self-centered one (7)
18 Composed satisfactory work about California (7)
19 Inside of Racine's radical, revolutionary element (7)
20 In vault, group of spies climbing on the shelf (7)
22 Head right for the pop (5)

ALFIO MICCI

A VIOLINIST WITH the New York Philharmonic for thirty years, Alfio Micci played under conductors Dimitri Mitropoulos, Leonard Bernstein, Zubin Mehta, and others. When the Philharmonic went on tour Micci took his crosswords with him. His fellow musicians knew how Micci spent his free time, but were still always surprised and delighted to see his by-line on the Sunday *New York Times* puzzles. On tour in Russia when one of his puzzles appeared in *The International Herald-Tribune,* Micci accepted the personal congratulations of conductor Erich Leinsdorf.

Although he retired from the Philharmonic in 1981, Micci is still very much involved in the music world. He participates in chamber concerts, gives solo performances, and records background music for television jingles.

Naturally enough, his first Sunday *Times* puzzle had a musical theme with these clues and answers:

Telephone sound	Bizet signal
Child's game	Haydn go seek
Question for a vanishing lady	Verdi she go
Postal warning	Handel with care

In another puzzle with a musical motif, Micci used puns based on operas:

Shaw play	Manon Superman
What do I do when I'm hungry?	Aida meal
Judy Garland movie	Mimi in St. Louis
Beginning of a well-known anthem	Jose Canio see

Micci's two careers started at different points in time and place, but gradually converged to a shared level of success. He began to study the violin when he was ten. A few years later he discovered crosswords. His parents didn't subscribe to a daily paper, but he visited an aunt who lived nearby and honed his solving skills on her copies of the *Chicago Tribune*. He did some minor constructing at this time, but only for family members, who, unfortunately, didn't share his enthusiasm for wordplay. Micci put his puzzles away for several years and concentrated on his music.

After high school Micci studied violin at the Eastman School of Music, earning both a bachelor's and master's degree there. During World War II he played with the U.S. Navy Band in Washington. He spent his spare time, not on frivolous wordplay, but on writing "several long, turgid plays on mostly seamy subjects, which upon rereading proved boring and totally without humor."

After his military discharge and search for career work in New York City, Micci opened his crossword files and started dabbling again. It was at this point that he sent his first puzzle to Margaret Farrar at *The New York Times*.

Micci's mastery of crosswords has made music for millions of solvers who delight in his clever definitions and themes. The numerous puzzles he constructs each year are found in the *Times,* Dell *Champion* magazines, syndicates edited by Herb Ettenson and James Boldt, and crossword series published by Running Press and Simon & Schuster.

Micci is adept at so many different types of crosswords that it's hard to identify him with one particular style. He has used rebuses, numbers, transpositions, hidden definitions, and other forms in his puzzles. Examples of selected themes and clues give some idea of the breadth of his talent.

From "Initial Offerings":

T	Beginning of time
EI	Pieces of eight
M	A quarter of a mile
D	Break of day
V	A fifth of vodka
N	A bit of news

From "Mathematricks":

120	Eight × fifteen
132	Twelve × eleven
3	Three × one
14	Seven × two

From "Gender Bender":

Golding title?	Lady of the flies
Henry Fonda flick?	Mrs. Roberts
Browning poem?	My last duke
Flying ace?	The Red Baroness
U.S. folk painter?	Grandpa Moses
Nursery rhyme character	Master Muffet

From "Getting There":

Drives	Line, sex, clothing and FDR
Walks	Cat, jay, cross and board
Runs	Home, trial, dry and rabbit
Cycles	Motor, mega, song and tri
Flies	Dragon, gad, horse and shoo

From "Not in the Family":

Fields	Marshall, Betty and Sally
Wests	Morris, Nathanael and Mae
Bergs	Gertrude, Patty and Alban
Fords	Tennessee Ernie and John
Whites	Stanford, Theodore and Deb

From "Plantation":

Fortunetellers	Palm readers
Harriet	Beecher Stowe
T. S. Eliot poem	Ash Wednesday
Iowa City	Cedar Rapids

From "Transpositions":

Be a lucky Broadway angel?	Spot the hit
Head, arms, legs, etc?	Parts of man
Illuminate the bishop's office?	Light the see
Workaholic's passion?	Love of labor

From "Inside Information":

Famallily	All in the family
=butwosh	Is worth two in the bush
Oholene	Hole in one

Boatakerders	Take in boarders
Becomesing	Comes into being
Indyeseed	Yes indeed

From "When in Rome":

In trouble	Behind the VIII ball
Meredith Wilson tune	LXXVI Trombones
Christie title	X Little Indians

From "Following Suits":

Triple-decker treat	♧ sandwich
Beth Henley play	Crimes of the ♡
Gay Nineties figure	◇ Jim Brady
Tchaikovsky opera	The Queen of ♤s

Micci constructs puzzles in the study of his home in Rutherford, New Jersey, where he has amassed a formidable library of atlases, almanacs, dictionaries, geographical and biographical references, and quotation books. "If you're a constructor, everybody gets you reference works for Christmas," says Micci.

Micci's wife, Martha, a pianist he met at the Eastman School, enjoys crosswords and helps him clue trivial information. Micci likes to discover unusual words and finds it natural to draw upon his musical knowledge for definitions or entries. For example, he prefers to define "Erie" and "Ani" respectively as "Soprano Mills" and "violinist Kavafian" instead of the overworked "Great Lake" and "blackbird."

(see next page for the puzzle)

COUNTRY LIFE by Alfio Micci

(SEE PAGE 264 FOR SOLUTION)

ACROSS

1 Miss St. Johns and namesakes
7 Violinist Mischa
12 Musical symbol
16 Brace
17 ''—— of Grass''
19 Coats for cooking
21 Brazzaville palms?
23 Film collie
24 Latin I word
25 Holds
26 Greek T
28 To be, in the Bois
29 Succinct
32 Giovanni or Pasquale
33 Call —— day
35 Awoke
37 FDR program
39 Masan mortgage?
42 Former White House lass
43 Author Nin
45 Christian or Roman
46 Carmichael
47 Porter
49 Wild horses
51 Cordage fiber
54 Indonesian isle
55 Farm unit
56 Boulogne barb
59 Pedro's uncle
61 Needlefish
63 Lumberjack, at times
65 Belgian province
67 Did housework
70 Summer cooler
71 Port-au-Prince allotment?
74 Stout
75 Hardy fowl
77 Rat
78 Casque
80 American Indian
81 Servicemen's org.
83 Exit
84 Despicable-sounding bottle
85 A Ladd
87 Sculpted works
89 Most like Tim
92 Aware of
93 Quotation word
94 Pouch
97 Patriot Silas
98 Nautical distance: abbr.
99 Amsterdam cupboard?
103 Scull
104 Run
106 U.K. coin, for short
107 —— Claire, Wis.
109 Yodeler's territory
113 Indian music
114 Printer's need
116 Very windy
119 Nice season
120 Threefold
122 Verona vessel?
126 Cheap cigar
127 Ruler
128 Prima ballerinas
129 Lop, in Loth
130 Actress-swimmer Williams, familiarly
131 Negligent

DOWN

1 Adler's *A House is Not* ——
2 Generous one
3 Work unit
4 Durocher
5 —— lang syne
6 Go over 55
7 A Roosevelt
8 Island off Timor
9 Hitchcock flick of '64
10 Collection of sacred writings
11 Formerly called
12 Ga.'s neighbor
13 Hare, in a fable
14 Sandgate stranger?
15 Oared vessel
16 Jazz form
18 JFK visitor
19 Galway's instrument
20 Ragged
22 Tend the furnace
27 —— a dream (unworldly)
30 Gershwin hit
31 Monumental
34 Indigo
36 Early Andean
38 Japanese volcano
40 Precipitation
41 Freedman
43 Shopping areas
44 Arendal army?
48 Korbut
49 Fundamental
50 ''Cervantes smiled —— chivalry away'' (Byron)
52 Members of a pool
53 Political extremist
54 Single-edged knife
57 Canadian prov.
58 Gleason's ''How Sweet ——!''
60 Least cordial
62 Free
64 Pi's follower
66 Ashen
68 Chang's twin
69 Started the card game
72 —— for one's money
73 ''—— the season . . .''

6 Aura
9 It's for the birds
2 Auricular
5 Time —— half
8 *Rosenkavalier* baron
Bachelor's last words
Undiluted
2 Lends
3 Anna who played Nana
5 Ester
5 Succession

98 Civil wrongs
100 Practical
101 "—— Heroes"
102 Palate portions
105 Scope
108 Austrian botanist Franz
110 Lively dances
111 Sioux
112 Wide-angle or zoom
115 Ewe's baby
117 Emphatic affirmative
from señora
118 Receipts
121 First or foreign
123 Ship's rope
124 Herbert of films
125 Full deck, in the Forum

ARNOLD MOSS

REGAL-LOOKING Arnold Moss—actor, writer, director, educator, and crossword constructor—gives a stellar performance in all his fields of endeavor. Puzzledom's only entrant in *Who's Who in America* melds his educational background and acting career to produce the most literate of puzzles.

Moss has an A.B. from The College of the City of New York, an A.M. from Columbia University, and a Ph.D. from New York University. His fields of concentration were Latin, Greek, and Old French. He also trained extensively with Eva LeGallienne's Civic Repertory Theatre.

His distinguished career as an actor in theater, film, and TV, most notably in Shakespearean dramas, earned him accolades from audiences all over the world. The role from which he's garnered the most publicity was that of Anton Koridian, a Shakespearean actor, in an episode of *Star Trek,* which seems to be repeated on TV "every fifteen minutes," according to Moss.

When Moss was in Luxor, Egypt, checking into a hotel prior to visiting the Valley of the Kings, he noticed a brouhaha at the registration desk. When the perplexed Moss asked if anything was wrong he was told, in broken English, "It is you, Mister. Last night you were on Egyptian TV—*Star Trek*!"

When Moss was the guest of honor at the 1985 Stamford Marriott Tournament, he participated in the Saturday evening group games before he was "officially" introduced to the contestants. Doug Heller, who was emceeing a trivia baseball game, knew Moss was in the audience and asked a player a prepared question that was to be answered by "Arnold Moss." After the contestant answered correctly, Heller pointed Moss out to the rest of the audience. When Rebecca Kornbluh, a top contestant who's normally shy and retiring, realized she was sitting in front of Moss she uncharacteristically screamed out, "That's Arnold Moss!"

Moss, who recently celebrated his seventy-fifth birthday, started to solve the crosswords in *The New York Herald Tribune* "a long time ago," and turned to constructing when he found the crosswords too easy to solve. He sold his first puzzle, a 23×23 titled "Capital Entertainment," to Margaret Farrar at the *Times*. "Each key word contained the name of a world capital which also related to entertainment, for example, Kingston Trio, Russ Colombo." Farrar "loved" the puzzle and encouraged Moss to keep constructing. He followed her advice and has been turning out literary, erudite crosswords since 1967.

Moss often cites the Bard in his crosswords. In "Classic Quotation" he fitted a quote from *Twelfth Night* into an unusually sized grid—18×18. The quote read "Many a good hanging prevents a bad marriage." In "An Appropriate Quotation," published in Farrar's calendar series, the quote he used was from *Julius Caesar* and read "Look in the calendar and bring me word."

Moss's quotes are not placed in traditional spots in the grid. In order to fit the *Twelfth Night* quote into the grid he broke up the word "prevents" after the "r." And he scattered the *Julius Caesar* quote in varied spots through the grid instead of presenting it horizontally and sequentially.

Moss creates puzzles in his "office at home—standing." He keeps a file folder of new ideas and works on a 15×15 for a week and a 21×21 for three to four weeks, in between his other work. The hardest part of constructing, he says, is "filling in the last empty space" and the best part is "the fun of discovering a word that solves a tough construction problem."

Moss often constructs puzzles where the theme is not readily apparent and is slowly revealed by solving the puzzle. In "Hard Stuff" for the Simon & Schuster series Farrar gave solvers a hint about the theme (metals) with her blurb: "Test your mettle against the hardly elementary problems." The themed clues were:

Swoons in electroplating plant	Zincing spells
English place of safety	London Palladium
Designating a 1930's shade	Platinum blond
Breakfast for writer Harry	A golden egg
Impost on tubas	Brass tacks

In "Willy-Nilly" Moss found a variety of ways to clue "Bill":

Valentine	Billet doux
Evangelist	Billy Sunday
Radio serial of the 1940's	Just plain Bill

Century	Hundred dollar bill
Bald as ——	A billiard ball
Errant man of song	Bill Bailey

Moss's favorite puzzle is one where he used original puns based on vegetables:

Cease-fire order	Lettuce have peas
Prestidigitator's request	Turnip a card
Wage reductions	Celery cuts

Actor/Constructor Arnold Moss awarded the prizes at the Ninth Annual Stamford Marriott Tournament.

Moss and his wife, Stella, travel extensively. He uses these trips as a takeoff for some of his crosswords. After a visit to the Soviet Union he constructed a ". . . With Love" crossword for *The Crossworder's Own Newletter*. The themed clues were "Russian ballets" ("Diaghilev offerings"); "Russian roulette" ("Dangerous game"); and "Russian steppes" ("Vast treeless tracts").

For the 1985 Stamford Marriott contest Moss constructed a "Who, What, and Where" crossword, subtitled "Around the World in 98 Words." The clues were similar to those he used in his very first crossword:

"All Alone" composer	Irving Berlin
Cole Porter musical of 1940	Panama Hattie
Call Me Mister composer (1946)	Harold Rome

Moss attended three Marriott tournaments as an honored guest, awarder of prizes, and constructor of a contest puzzle. He enjoyed watching the mechanics of the contest and was especially interested in the final round, in which the top three contestants compete in a sudden-death playoff. Only a small percentage of solvers reach the playoffs. Those who do are extremely serious about winning and train rigorously for the competitions. Most solvers realize that they have no chance of winning and attend contests for the camaraderie and opportunities to solve excellent puzzles.

Successfully bridging the gap between the acting and crossword worlds, Moss certainly has the "write stuff" for crossword construction.

SIGHT AND SOUND by Arnold Moss

(SEE PAGE 265 FOR SOLUTION)

ACROSS

1 John and Jas.
4 Italian kingdoms
9 Didn't own
14 Overact, in a way
17 With 40 Across, NYC's mayor, 1901
18 Self-centeredness
20 Certain charms
22 Chem. ending
23 —— *for the Money*
24 BYY
26 TV's "messages"
27 Snout beetle
29 Hawaiian winds
30 "—— her that . . . for your love" (Shak.)
32 Of a kind of lens
34 Poet Allen and playwright Nahum
36 Milk: comb. form
37 Electric generators
40 See 17 Across
41 Bunyan and Og
44 Jackie's second
45 Body shop's concerns
47 A place to rule
50 Rye disease
51 Yukon or N.W.
53 Jorge's hobby
55 Winnie et al.
57 Musical notation
58 Hawthorne's home
60 Star of *The Seven Year Itch*
62 "—— low, if you . . . love" (Shak.)
64 Spire finial
65 To —— (everybody)
67 Weight dice
69 Kind of event
71 Berlin news, 1948–49
74 —— luxury (bed of roses)
76 Supervise
77 At a —— (in demand)
78 Seaport in Portugal
79 Item for B.S.A.
80 School of whales
81 "Whom shall ——?" (Isaiah)
84 0
86 Famed N.Y. restaurateur
90 Bambi's aunt et al.
92 What Villon missed
94 "See ya" in Siena
95 ". . . troubles I've ——"
96 Slangy negatives
98 —— *Entertainment*
100 One of a pair by Gluck
103 Cribbage item
104 Buy back
106 Frolic
108 Bicyclist's disaster
110 Tightly packaged
112 Cenobite
114 Kind of wool
115 Of Peter Martin's world
118 Stiller's partner
120 American poet John Crowe, 1888–1974
123 Homonym for "aura"
124 KC
127 Wedding vow
128 Tome: abbr.
129 More stylish
130 Ink makers
131 Amer. legionnaire
132 Asian fighter of the 50s
133 ". . . forgive us our ——" (Matthew)
134 *Uncle Vanya* role
135 Cannibalize

DOWN

1 Adagio
2 Star of *Hotel Universe*
3 QT
4 Altered electrical work
5 One of a French trio
6 "I —— Rhythm"
7 Nora's "Thin Man"
8 "—— an arrow . . ." (Longfellow)
9 Stork's hangout
10 1st name, 16th Pres.
11 Offspring: abbr.
12 Where Durban is
13 Chew —— (make small talk)
14 MT
15 Take apart
16 Impresario Morris, 1881–1942
19 Talking birds
21 Coins
25 Horse opera
28 —— Karajan
31 Vesper and Sirius
33 EE
35 Chases away
37 P.M. shows
38 Rectangle's length × breadth
39 Brunswick, e.g.
42 Rug, to some
43 Take in one's —— (cope with)
46 Characteristic of SO_2
48 Hush money
49 UNI
52 Sway
54 "Half —— is better . . ."
56 Greetings from Gaius
59 Near future date
61 Mexican resort city
63 Bemoans
66 Make —— (complain)
68 Kind of column
70 Mlles. of Merida

1 Materialize
2 Literary device for René
3 CC
5 Shakespeare's first
2 Edo drama
3 Bonsai, e.g.
5 Goldfish
7 ODS
8 Musk or fallow
9 Once dean of St. Paul's
1 What Hank Aaron used to do

93 Attackers
97 Choice
99 Widgeons
101 Uniformity
102 South Pacific
105 School of acting
107 Home for Goyas
109 Lacrosse team
111 Sawyer of "60 Minutes"
113 Sevareid and Portman

115 Warrior at Mafeking
116 Pisa's river
117 Plagiarize
119 Type of saxaphone
121 Music halls
122 Street in N.Y.'s Chinatown
125 Impediment
126 He played Quasimodo

STANLEY NEWMAN

When Stanley Newman first started to solve crosswords it took him "forever" to finish a 21×21 puzzle. By 1982 he had earned the "world's fastest solver" title after whizzing through a *New York Times* daily puzzle in two minutes, twenty-four seconds while being filmed by an NBC news crew for a TV show. Although that record has never been broken, Newman no longer clocks himself on the two dozen puzzles he solves per week, for his crossword energies are now channeled into constructing, editing and directing tournaments.

Still in his early thirties, Newman has fashioned a second career for himself that looks as promising as his official one: bond analyst for a major investment company. The rapid transition from neophyte to professional in the crossword world was a direct result of his prowess in the contest arena.

Newman honed his solving skills on crosswords in *TV Guide* as a child and *The New York Times* as a teenager. He suspected that he was a fast solver, but it wasn't until the fourth Stamford Marriott competition (1981) that he got confirmation of this. His very respectable thirteenth-place finish satisfied his curiosity as to how he measured up against the pros. After finishing fifth at Grossinger's Crossword Weekend one month later, he had a serious case of the "solving bug."

Newman decided to train rigorously for the next competition, ten months away. He firmly believes that crossword competitors should prepare for tournaments as methodically as athletes prepare for meets. His mental marathon included solving 1,500 puzzles during this time, looking up each unfamiliar word in the dictionary and timing himself on every puzzle (a valuable pointer he had picked up from Miriam Raphael, a frequent competition winner). His efforts were rewarded triply with back-to-back-to-back wins at the Marriott, Grossinger's, and *Games*'s U.S. Open in 1982. Newman had achieved a first—winning the "grand slam" of crossword contests.

Racing through a particularly gimmicky set of puzzles at Stamford in '82, Newman solved Threba Johnson's riddle—"What does Confucius say about early Christmas presents?" "No Peking"—and figured out that the trick to Stephanie Spadaccini's "Crossword Plus" puzzle was to insert an ampersand in the grid so that "Pen & ink" could cross with "Mr. & Mrs." and "Time & tide" with "Five & ten."

Newman was to be victorious in two other tournaments (Grossinger's in 1983 and Los Angeles in 1985) before "retiring" from crossword contests.

Between 1980 and 1983 Grossinger's resort hotel sponsored four crossword weekends. Will Weng and Eugene Maleska were the honored guests at two of these fests and treated guests to a behind-the-scenes look at the *Times* crossword. Other events during the four years included a puzzle slide show, crossword quiz, "Boggle" and "Password" competitions, hints on solving cryptic crosswords and crossword contests. All the weekends were under the expert direction of Will Shortz.

As Newman racked up his impressive wins his friends urged him to parlay them into a business enterprise. Coincidentally, during this same period, Shortz was encouraging Newman to become a crossword constructor.

Bowing to this delightful pressure, Newman embarked on several ventures in 1982. He formed the American Crossword Federation (ACF) to "foster the development of contemporary crosswords as a medium of entertainment and challenge," wrote and published *The Ultimate Crossword Book* (a collection of graded puzzles that enable puzzlers to determine their level of tournament solving skill) and started *The Crossworder's Own Newsletter*.

The newsletter, issued under the auspices of the ACF, provides Newman with a forum to reach his one thousand "hard-core, very serious" subscribers. This insiders' publication contains six different levels of crosswords. Examples indicate the shaded differences separating each level and Newman's ability to clue familiar words in a novel way:

Level 1—Puzzler

Macintosh throwaways	Cores
Scratch target	Itch
Assembly line newcomer	Robot

Horny brother?	Elk
Hippie greeting	Peace
Flat rate	Rent

Level 2—Middler

Old Olds	Reo
Bar order	Usual
Man in a cage	Teller
Lobster eaters' extras	Bibs
24 days to Xmas	Dec. 1
—— Turn (highway sign)	No U

Level 3—Expert

Light-headed?	Fair
Get it all together?	Stir
Smart partner?	Agent 99
Hardly the big shot	BBs
Diamond termini?	Dees

Level 4—Master

Oil vessel?	Lamp
Conductor's announcement	All off
Refrain from childhood	EIEIO
Mr. Moss?	Peat
Ad ending, perhaps	Act now
The whole dictionary	A to Z

Level 5—Grand Master

Supreme commander?	Ross
Meter maid?	Poet
Dog tag?	Fido
It brings people closer	Zoom
China in the afternoon	Tea set

Level 6—Champion

March man	St. Pat
Unauthorized TV greeting	Hi Ma
Got more power	Rewired
Cab cutter?	Hacksaw

The newsletter also contains book reviews, articles about puzzle people, information about what's happening in the puzzle world, and wordplay contests. "Crossword Confidential" is probably the only gossip column of its kind. Newman sees the newsletter as a forum for constructors and solvers to discuss the finer points of crosswords, an opportunity not available elsewhere.

He also uses the newsletter as a place to try out new ideas such as Merl Reagle's "Something Different" puzzle, which contained answers that weren't dictionary entries yet were valid in their own way. Examples included:

Yak test	Ox experiment
Do without illustrations	Use no art
The eighth wise man	Sage H
Grizzly gulch, for example	Bear area

Solvers' responses to this unconventional puzzle ranged from "too extreme" and "utterly boring" to "a breath of freshly skewed air" and "challenging, yet not as difficult as it appears at first sight."

His "Film Clip" contest, in which contestants removed a single letter from a movie title and clued it humorously, generated a flood of responses that included these winning entries:

"Just a girl who can't say nyet?" *Anne of the Thousand Das*
"Cryophysics?" *The Ion in Winter*
"Adam and Eve, together again?" *Forbidden Plant*
"Story of a Supernova?" *Star Was*
"Daring presidential impersonation?" *The Man in the Ron Mask*
"The first headache?" *The Greatest Story Eve Told*
"Daytime funnyman?" *Wit Until Dark*

Newman devotes at least twenty hours per week to his second career. In addition to the newsletter, he edits several collections of crosswords and constructs individualized crosswords for company newsletters.

The third aspect of Newman's crossword career is directing crossword tournaments. The Presenting Baltimore Annual Crossword Open debuted in February 1986 and will be held annually sometime in the first half of the year. The North Jersey Crossword Open is held in early June in the Riverside Square Shopping

Center in Hackensack, New Jersey. Both contests are sponsored by the ACF.

Newman believes that tournaments are "a showcase for solvers to see clever, humorous puzzles that require knowledge of the contemporary world." Recognizing that some solvers may be familiar only with crosswords using factual definitions, Newman makes an effort to commission puzzles with a "twist" for his tournaments. Thus, in the first Baltimore tourney Mel Rosen's "Position Wanted" crossword included seven entries clued as "See [another entry]." Solvers had to determine the relationships between these pairs of answers. When the diagram was completed the positioning of the words formed a familiar phrase. For example:

```
S S    WRAPS     HEAD      NOT
I I    KEPT      HEELS     A  BET
D D
E E
       THE BED     MIND        STANDING
       LOOK        MATTER      CEREMONY
```

translated respectively into: "side by side," "kept under wraps," "head over heels," "not on a bet," "look under the bed," "mind over matter," and "standing on ceremony."

Henry Hook's (see page 66) "My Whole Is Your Goal" puzzle was a little more devious—contestants had to determine a bonus word through a three-step process. First, they solved a crossword in which four of the long entries yielded definitions of five-letter words. Each of these words was composed of five of the letters in the bonus word; these letters were indicated merely by their numerical position in the bonus word. For example, one clue, "My 3-8-10-1-6 is ——" yielded the answer, "chop into small pieces," which defined "mince." The third, eighth, tenth, first, and sixth letters of the bonus word were M, I, N, C, and E respectively. The bonus word was "completion," and solvers who figured out this word earned 100 bonus points for their efforts.

Tournament winner David Rosen sped through this puzzle in twelve minutes while others needed twelve minutes just to figure out the gimmick! No stranger to the winner's circle (he won several tournaments), Rosen is a young, mild-mannered insurance

Tournament director Stan Newman greets the contestants prior to the first round of solving at the first Presenting Baltimore Open.

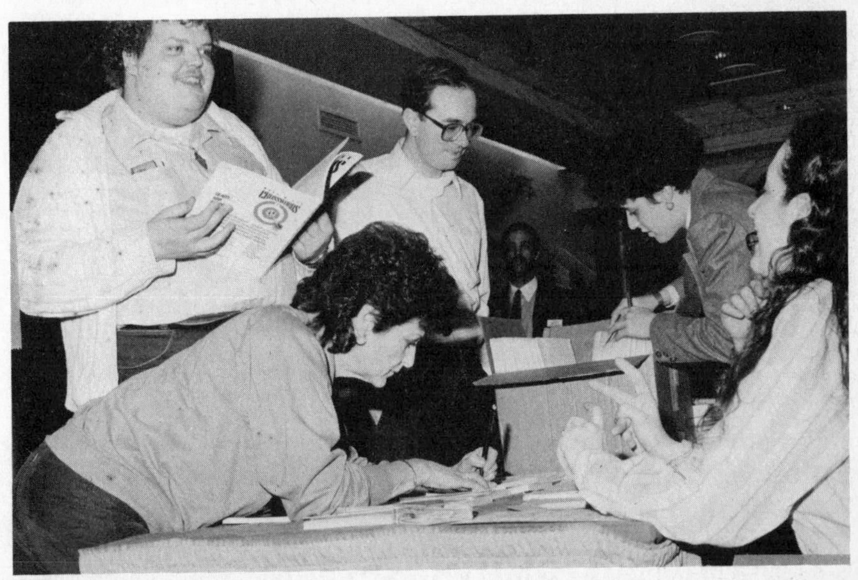

Judges Nancy Schuster (left) and Stephanie Abrams-Hook (seated right) register contestants Bill Hendricks (left) and David Rosen.

executive from New York City with a passion for crosswords. His heavy workload doesn't allow him a lot of time to train for tournaments, but he does time himself on every puzzle he solves. Like most contestants he's drawn to competitions for the camaraderie:

"While some of us are more intense about winning than others, I enjoy being with anybody who's enamored of my pastime. What's more, although it's a low-visibility, low-prize 'sport,' it gives me a satisfying feeling to realize that I am one of the best in the country at something that I enjoy doing."

Newman makes every effort to meet and talk with all the constructors who supply him with puzzles for his ventures, thereby allowing him to share his enthusiasm for "contemporary" crosswords with these suppliers. For Newman is a staunch advocate of wordplay that entertains and challenges without being obscure. He sees himself as "a conduit" through which he can make more people aware of these crosswords.

The intense Newman is more intense, and even militant, when discussing his philosophy of crossword constructing and editing. His putting-the-solver-first philosophy translates: "A solver who likes crosswords doesn't want to see Chinese measures and historic figures he's never heard of. Keeping obscure words in puzzles is unforgivable. Having edited several hundred puzzles I believe that most 'crosswordese' can be changed." Newman will spend as long as necessary to eliminate the "crosswordese" out of his puzzles. But if he must include a word such as "alai" he'll clue it familiarly as "jai ——" and never as "Asian mountain."

Newman's favorite clues are those that are humorous yet factually correct:

It's inspired	Air
He likes big busts	Narc
State secrets	Snitch
Beer barrel poker	Tap
Relief pitcher	Ade

Newman's days are taken up with both his careers. While he's at work all his energies are directed toward his job. The puzzler part of him emerges on the train ride home between New York City and Massapequa, New York, as he constructs 15 × 15 crosswords. His goal is to construct one such puzzle each evening. He works only on the grid, saving the cluing and finishing touches for evenings and weekends.

Contestant Tom Fuller concentrates on solving during a tournament round.

Contestant Vincent Bonzagni checks his ranking prior to the final solving round.

David Rosen, winner of numerous tournaments, solving the playoff puzzle during the 1986 Presenting Baltimore Open

At home, he works in a study filled with extensive reference works and more than three hundred crossword books, allowing him to check all facts in-house. Newman is especially proud of his library because he's always felt that he should be able to answer any questions with the books he has in his own home.

Stanley Newman sees crosswords in a different light from many other constructors and editors. The businessman in him believes that big-money crossword tournaments can become a reality if crossword-solving corporate presidents become aware of crossword tournaments and if crosswords are packaged properly for TV.

Newman's dual career is gliding along smoothly on both tracks now. But he finds it comforting to know that "if Wall Street goes kaput" he could support his wife and three young children on crosswords alone.

KITTY LITTER by Stanley Newman

(SEE PAGE 265 FOR SOLUTION)

ACROSS

1 *Vive's* opposite
5 "Prime" rater: abbr.
9 Rock band instrument
13 Most relevant
19 Minimum change
20 Speedily
21 —— cost (free)
22 La-di-da
23 Visit Tiger Stadium with kitty?
27 ". . . wonder, —— night"
28 —— Monte
29 Replace a puzzle's crosswordese
30 Tiny bits
31 *Entre* ——
33 Elemental prefix
35 CIA predecessor
37 Singer Lane
40 Feline shirking?
48 Turns testy
50 Gun lobby: abbr.
51 Gilda
52 A head of *Time*
53 Related
54 Baseball commish, in headlines
56 Sauces sources
57 More calculating
58 Elude feline wrath?
61 Feline musical?
64 Finish modernizing the store
65 Mother of the Titans
67 Fifth word of "America"
68 Mr. Pulver's rank
69 Thespian
72 Schmaltz
75 "The —— Daba Honeymoon"
78 Mechanical processor
79 Second glove
81 Bring charges
85 Employee of CBS Mews?
88 Lost feline?
91 Not broadside
92 Goldfinger
94 Pillar
95 Mare mama
96 Summers in Sèvres
97 —— one's feet
99 Pou ——
100 Pinnacle
102 Feline's looking for trouble?
106 Stop exercising
107 What a feller needs
108 Funny Johnson
109 Korbut
111 Judge, often
115 Optimal
118 Springfield nickname
120 Pacific island
124 Feline ape?
128 Lansbury
129 Part of RCA
130 Network junction
131 He likes big busts
132 Some of Brother's kids
133 Georgetown athlete
134 Country Campbell
135 Modern artist

DOWN

1 Cabaret performances
2 Tuckered out
3 "My Way" writer
4 "Ambition should be made of —— stuff"
5 Availing
6 —— Canals
7 *Harvey* hero
8 Reception aid
9 Stoop item
10 North, to south
11 Unified
12 Asian desert
13 A Coast: abbr.
14 Refinement
15 Diner order
16 —— *-major* (headquarters: Fr.)
17 Pre-Rubik cube
18 Piggies, maybe
24 Alley Oop's land
25 Smelly
26 Set things right
32 Chinese
34 Knobby
36 Ship type: abbr.
37 "Jeopardy" contestant, often
38 Northwest capital
39 Swindle
41 Russian city
42 Theodore Roosevelt Nat'l Park state
43 Kind of inspection
44 Fashion mag
45 Power
46 Unlimited quantity
47 Convy and Parks
49 Metropolis protector
55 '84 Olympic Marathon winner Joan
56 Bees in transit
57 Sense utility trouble
59 *6 Rms Riv Vu* setting
60 Generation
62 —— Na Na
63 Circle intersector
66 Athenian
70 Extreme: abbr.
71 Be the will of
73 Hse.
74 Plumber's joint
75 ". . . golden crown like —— well" (Shak.)
76 African tongue
77 Where llamas live

80 C major's analog
82 Gorme
83 Snarls
84 Kranepool or Harrelson
86 Supreme commander?
87 Monotonous states
89 Former Japanese P.M.
90 During gestation
93 Alternating
97 *Back to the Future* star
98 It multiplies by dividing
99 Affair
101 Almond candy
103 Lombard
104 WKRP, et al.
105 Bears or Rams
110 Day- —— (fluorescent chemical)
111 Fed
112 Hindu queen
113 *Bus Stop* playwright
114 CEO, e.g.
116 —— -A-Sketch (drawing toy)
117 ''Scramola!''
119 Hydroxyl compound
121 —— garage
122 Half of CD
123 Coal conclusion
125 Mis' followers
126 ''—— Lazy River''
127 5-star monogram

CONSTRUCTING A 15×15 crossword around the following verse by James Thurber:

> Early to rise,
> Early to bed,
> Makes a man healthy,
> Wealthy, and dead.

Tap Osborn sent it to Will Weng at *The New York Times*. Weng loved the puzzle but was reluctant to use it without permission from the Thurber estate. Weng's hesitation was well-founded because when an Ogden Nash verse had been used in a similar manner the Nash estate "made a lot of noise" and threatened to sue the *Times*.

When Osborn explained this to Mrs. Thurber, she readily gave him the necessary permission. "The last thing I want is to upset *The New York Times,*" she wrote. Osborn went to all that trouble for $15.00, the amount the *Times* paid at that time for its daily crosswords.

Osborn sent his first puzzle, based on Robert Frost's "Stopping by Woods on a Snowy Evening," to Weng at the *Times* in 1972. He vividly remembers the elation he felt when Weng replied that he would accept the puzzle if Osborn made some minor alterations. "Will asked me to change a couple of things, then he would run it. I did and he did, thus launching my career. In the next year he ran nine of my dailies!"

Osborn rarely uses other writers' verses anymore, preferring to compose his own poetry. Each of his verses contains the same number of letters in each line because they must fit into a "standard" size grid, e.g., 19×19, 23×23, etc. His poetic themes range from fatherhood:

> The gifts we shower Dad with,
> The ones supposed to thrill,
> Are met with mixed emotions
> 'Cause he also foots the bill!

to politics:

> A political hack did bewail
> His fate in sending out mail
> That contained some advice
> Plus some cash to vote twice.
> Today he's running from jail.

Osborn constructs crosswords in his den at home or in an easy chair while watching television. In 1985 he retired from a thirty-seven-year career with Reed and Barton Silversmiths and now devotes all of his working time to constructing and editing crosswords. Divorced, with five grown children, he divides his time between his homes in East Falmouth, Massachusetts, and Sanibel, Florida. He edits the Pen and Pencil series for Running Press and constructs crosswords for a variety of other publishers, syndicates, editors, and contest coordinators. In his spare time he plays tennis and bridge and reads voraciously.

His favorite crosswords are those with humorous themes or unusual definitions. His very favorite puzzle, originally titled "Famous Last Words," but printed as "Phony Finales," was based on punny departing lines by well-known people:

Napoleon's last words?	Make mine a short bier
Epitaph for Icarus?	Don't be a soar loser
Posthumous book by Bonnie?	The Yegg and I
Rommel's last words?	Tunis anyone
Trotsky's last words?	The end is incite
Composer's last words?	The Bach stops here
Hobo king Livingstone's last words?	Farewell to alms

In "Double Takes" he gave new meanings to famous quotes:

Here comes the judge	Honorable mention
How sharper than a serpent's tooth	Pained expression
Et tu Brute!	Cutting remark
Soak the rich!	Tax declaration

The theme of his "Near Misses" crossword was films that didn't win the Academy Awards. These were all clued as "Non-Oscar winner'' with the appropriate date. Answers included *The Tunnel on the River Kwai, The German Connection, How Brown Was My Valley, In the Cold of the Night, An Englishman in Paris,* and *The Worst Years of Our Lives.*

Osborn used a visual gimmick, a picture of a sun instead of the word ''sun'' in ''Shedding Light,'' published in the *New York Times* crossword books. Will Weng's blurb gave solvers a broad hint, ''The gimmick should dawn on the solver fairly quickly.'' Clues included:

Sliding car-top	✹ roof
Ra or Helios	✹ God
Butch Cassidy's friend	✹ dance kid
Breakfast dish option	Eggs ✹ny side up

Visual gimmicks have been used in crosswords on a limited basis. Solvers who love them appreciate the humor, but those who don't catch on to the gimmick really can't ''solve'' the puzzle or find anything but cross words to say about it.

Will Shortz started the opening round of the 1986 Stamford Marriott Tournament with Ferni Kinnaw's ''Give Us the High Sign'' crossword in which solvers had to replace the word ''star'' with an asterisk (*). Almost every contestant ''got'' the gimmick for it was clued appropriately—''A warm-up puzzle with a suitably light touch''—and the themed entries weren't too difficult:

Young actress	*let
Jolt	*tle
Chicken of the Sea competitor	* Kist
TV's —— *Galactica*	Battle *

Constructors who devise puzzles like this assume that solvers have a sense of humor and will catch on to the gimmick when they see fewer spaces allotted for familiar definitions. Thus, the fact that the answer to ''Captain Kirk's series'' has only five letters should be enough to clue the solver in to the gimmick, for it's assumed that he or she will readily recognize the answer as *Star Trek.*

Almost every contestant at the Marriott caught on to the gimmick and finished the puzzle. One of the few contestants who didn't see the light on this puzzle finished the tournament at the bottom of the rankings. His spirits weren't dampened too much, however—he offered to write the "backword" for this book!

Osborn asked solvers to do a double take with his "First the Good News . . ." crossword. Here solvers discovered a happy prophecy in one themed answer and its deflating counterpart in another, e.g., "Global tensions will ease" followed by "at both the polar regions"; "Air pollution will abate" . . . "as energy shortages grow"; and "Congress will toil as one" . . . "to vote itself a pay raise."

He also asks solvers to think creatively when they answer his nontraditional clues:

Sound sleeper?	Snorer
Future swimmers	Roe
Pig's digs	Pen
What Bo is	Aten
What Peggy is	Alee

Osborn created some of the crossword puzzles that were used in several of the tournaments sponsored by the Friends of the Dartmouth Libraries and conducted by Eugene Maleska. These contests began in 1979 and are small, low-keyed affairs which usually attract local competitors.

Tap Osborn has many personal fond memories of his experiences in the crossword world. He is most proud of his first Sunday puzzle in *The New York Times* and his appointment as editor of the Running Press crossword series, The Pen and Pencil Club, through which he's published eight books.

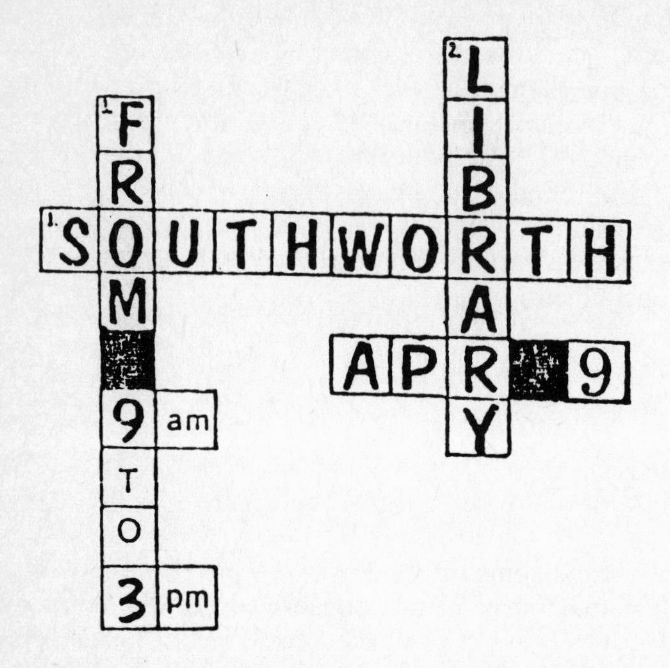

Flyer for the tournament sponsored by the Friends of the Dartmouth Libraries and coordinated by Tap Osborn

(see next page for the puzzle)

UPS AND DOWNS by Tap Osborn

(SEE PAGE 265 FOR SOLUTION)

ACROSS

1 "—— on earth, good . . ."
6 Where the local stops
11 He cut a lot of ice once
14 Spectral body
19 Hindu souls
20 Elliptic molding
21 Despair
22 Hokkaido port
23 It goes up and down
25 It goes up or down
27 Stranger
28 —— Speedwagon
29 Italian composer (1847–1916)
30 Gray or Moran of TV
31 Govt. agts.
33 Overly collegiate
36 Perlman of "Cheers"
40 Hack
42 One who goes up and down at work
44 Hair holder
45 Alma- ——, USSR
47 Word with St. Louis
49 Give goose bumps to
50 Raspy
51 Usurers, e.g.
53 Impromptu remark
54 Reinforce
55 Early on
56 Eero's father
57 Throng
58 Marquand title name
59 Graduation march composer
60 Vagrants
61 Crested duck
65 Teaching org.
66 One who has ups and downs, usually
70 Site of the Tell legend
71 Is he a safe man? Yes and no.
73 Learning system
74 Movie old-timer Jack
75 Pro quarterback Tony
77 Start of a Dickens title
79 Vied at Sebring
80 Big step
81 Abbey haircut
84 Woodsy areas
85 Poet Geoffrey
86 Like croplands
87 Do a chef's job
88 Noise that makes a cat tense
89 Malabar measure
90 Punishable
91 It goes up and then down
93 Annex
95 Israel's airline
96 Corn-crop worker
97 Bristol bye-bye
99 Kind of prof.
102 Most minimal
104 Douglas is one
105 East Indian sailor
107 It goes up and down
111 It goes up and down
113 Dialect
114 Poet's word
115 Choler
116 *Pia mater* folds
117 Daft
118 War medal, briefly
119 Down to a few bucks
120 He wrote *Golden Boy*

DOWN

1 Food for *le chien*
2 Early anesthesia
3 It goes up and down
4 Keel-shaped ridge
5 Salinger heroine
6 DeLuise
7 Hilary's conquest
8 Powerful
9 It makes toast tastier
10 Hilltop rock pile
11 Have an IOU
12 Dais
13 Brush on more polyurethane
14 Future trotter
15 These go up and down
16 Tit for ——
17 Nigerian native
18 Play about robots
24 Leftover
26 Bat wood
32 Bernstein opus
33 It goes up and down
34 "For want of —— . . ."
35 Bedouin tribe
37 Lorenz or Gary
38 "What —— is new?"
39 Takeoff artist
41 Wallace and Noah
43 Top tire
44 Auction word
45 Cuomo's power base
46 Home on the range
48 Land measure
50 Pet for Jackie
52 Richard or Jane
53 Kelp et al.
54 Frozen dessert
56 Upper crust
57 Muggy
59 *Académie,* e.g.
60 Transports for one or two
62 It goes up and down
63 Rust-encrusted
64 Vineyards adjunct

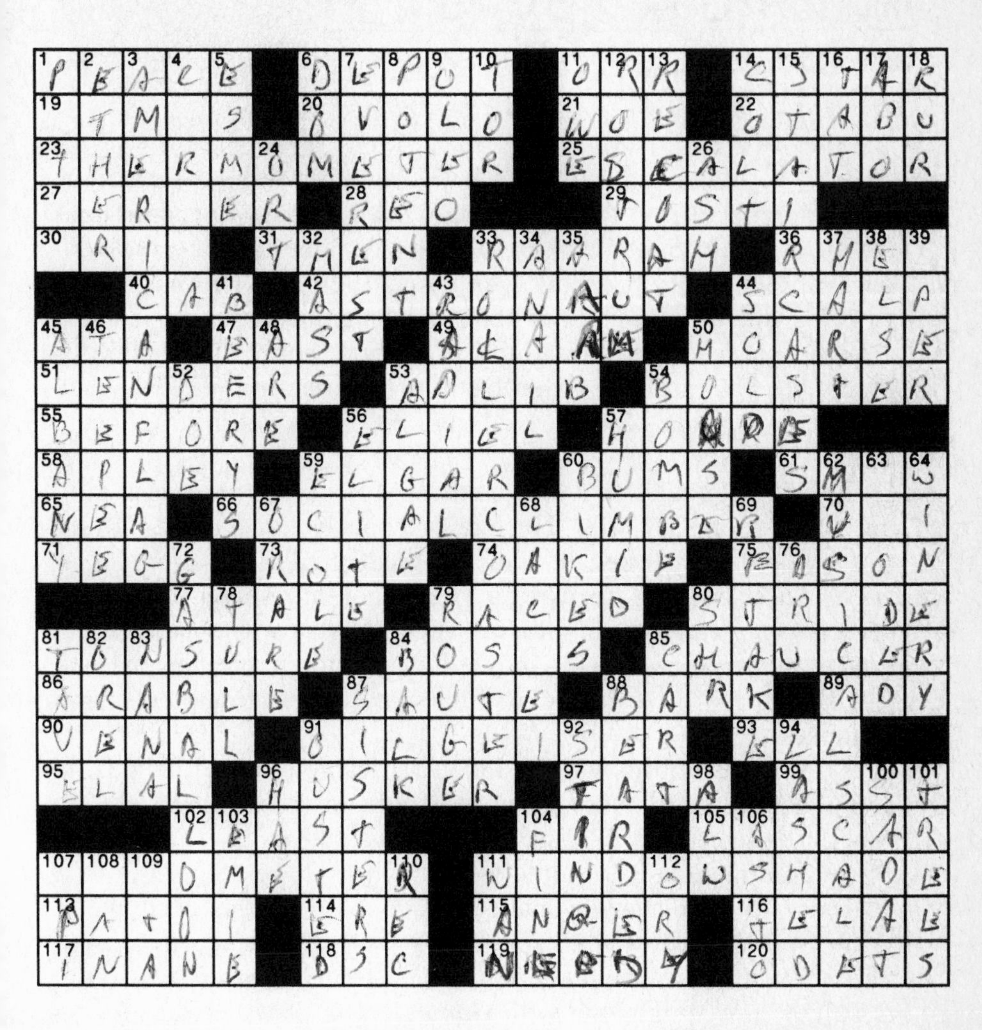

67 "—— Ben Jonson!"
68 Toady
69 Filming shoot
72 It goes up, then down
76 "Indeed!," in Cork
78 Jethro ——, seed-sowing machine inventor
79 Cheek colorer
80 Stock unit, briefly
81 What Coe breaks
82 Pitcher Hersheimer
83 Zola lady
84 Mound gaffe
85 Shopping aid
87 *The Three* ——
88 Groomed like Grant
91 Ejected
92 Be close-fisted
94 Tied securely
96 Own, to Angus
98 Kind of horse race: abbr.
100 He came before Mubarak
101 Famed poem
103 TV prize
104 Court collection
106 Concerning
107 Puppeteer Baird
108 Foofaraw
109 Raoul's river
110 —— room
111 Pallid
112 Rich in minerals

MERL REAGLE

EVERY WEEKDAY MORNING at 6:30 Merl Reagle arrives at Fromin's Deli, on the corner of Wilshire Boulevard and Nineteenth Street in Santa Monica, sits at the same table by the window, orders a light breakfast—and constructs crosswords. If he's working on the clues rather than the diagram he'll tote along a few dictionaries. He stays for two or three hours and then goes home. He has rarely deviated from this routine in the eight years he's been in Santa Monica. He thinks Fromin's is "the best place to work."

Reagle originally moved to Santa Monica for reasons totally unrelated to crosswords. He had previously lived in San Francisco where he worked in a movie theater as an assistant manager. An aspiring screenwriter, he spent his spare time on a screenplay. After nine months of work the play was complete and Reagle moved closer to the movie industry to pursue his goal. He free-lanced for three years, writing screenplays, treatments, and synopses.

To supplement his writing income, Reagle pursued his puzzle activities. He had been earning money from crosswords since he was a teenager, but because the pay was so paltry, he'd never considered making it full-time work.

But *Games* magazine made its debut during his Hollywood years, and Reagle was so impressed with it that he wrote Will Shortz, told him of his experience, and thereby began a working relationship with him and with *Games*.

Reagle was also interested in the puzzle tournament scene and flew to Stamford, Connecticut, in March 1979 to enter the second Marriott Tournament. He won third prize, but the real prize for him was meeting two of the people with whom he had corresponded and for whom he had constructed puzzles—Margaret Farrar, retired editor at *The New York Times,* and Rosalind Moore, editor in chief of Dell Publishing Company's puzzle magazines. Farrar's first words to him were in reference to his beard. "You're much hairier than I thought you'd be," she said.

Reagle had been selling his puzzles to Farrar for fifteen years, ever since he was a fifteen-year-old. But Reagle's involvement with crosswords dates back even further—he was an early reader who also loved to make up his own puzzles and word games. His mother bought him a subscription to *Highlights for Children,* which contained crossword puzzles, and Reagle started to solve those. He graduated to the syndicated crossword in his local newspaper. This crossword had a grid eleven boxes across and thirteen boxes down and for many years was the only crossword he worked. He was astounded the first time that he saw two eleven-letter words filling the top two rows—he didn't know that such relationships were possible.

Reagle started to make up his own crosswords using the diagrams in the local paper. He often went to his grandmother's house and spent a lot of time with her copy of the first edition of *Webster's New International Dictionary*. His grandmother would hand him the dictionary and tell him to "go and play." Reagle would read the dictionary and put words into puzzles. He started to make some "strange word interlocks." After fitting a few words together, he would look through the dictionary to find filler words to fit in the missing spaces. Although the words he used would never be used in a crossword (they were much too obscure), the remarkable thing that Reagle discovered was the unlimited possibilities of word interlocking. He wanted to flex his brain and wondered how far he could go.

When Reagle first saw wide-open patterns (those with very few black spaces) he immediately began to compose his own variations. He recalls, "I thought the more wide open it could be, the more startling it would look. It didn't occur to me that word choice was important until I started to send my puzzles to Margaret Farrar."

Reagle had sold one puzzle before sending his crosswords to Farrar. It was in *World Week* magazine and earned him $10.00. After getting that acceptance he mailed off three 15 × 15 puzzles, all with wide-open diagrams, to Farrar. She immediately rejected two of the puzzles for they didn't contain "very entertaining thoughts." Reagle had used expressions like "dead as a doornail" and "rotten in Denmark" in one puzzle and had included "edema" in the other. Farrar's dictum was to reject puzzles with references to "death, disease, war, and taxes." She felt that many solvers were commuters and the "subway solver doesn't want those things in his puzzles."

Farrar accepted Reagle's third puzzle. He quips, "I accidentally did nothing wrong in that puzzle." Farrar called the puzzle, with its triple fifteen-letter phrases down the center, a remarkable "*tour de force*" for a fifteen-year-old. Wide-open diagrams became his trademark.

When Reagle started to send his crosswords to Will Shortz at *Games,* Shortz told him that his word choices were questionable and "took away from the beauty of my diagrams." Reagle started to study the puzzles produced by Henry Hook (see page 66) and Mike Shenk (see page 186). Reagle feels that these two constructors were the biggest influences on his work.

Reagle was impressed with Hook's "alphabet soup" diagrams. "He would place words like FTDIXNJ into a grid. At first I'd think it was an obscure entry until I examined it and found that it was an abbreviation for 'Fort Dix, New Jersey.' " Reagle felt that this "was a fair and tricky clue and absolutely brilliant." Reagle remembered his feeling of astonishment when he discovered entries like these in Hook's puzzles. "That was one aspect of puzzles I had missed completely. The answer was easy, but it looked hard."

Shenk's contribution to Reagle's growth came from his philosophy that even three-letter words had to be "words." "Shenk felt that a truly talented constructor would not resort to unusual abbreviations or acronyms for his three-letter entries. He felt that a constructor should never slough off, even with small entry words."

Reagle developed his own unique style, a blend of the philosophies espoused by Hook and Shenk with the special Reagle twist, e.g., use of odd letters of the alphabet, wide-open diagrams, new-wave clues, and creative themes.

Reagle likes to use letters like J, Q, X, and Z in his puzzles for he feels that these letters are always trying to get into the diagrams and nobody will allow them to enter. Reagle's puzzles are truly extraordinary for he not only includes these "orphan" letters, but he places them in a wide-open diagram based on a creative theme.

For example, his "Biting Wit" crossword for the fifth Stamford Marriott Tournament was based on a "comment by Will Rogers" (one themed entry) "about the Venus de Milo" (another themed entry). The quote, positioned in the middle three horizontal rows, read "See what'll happen if you don't stop biting your fingernails." In addition, the puzzle contained the following words—"indexer," "kiwi," "jade," "coccyx"—and phrases—"in a jam," "take 10," "at 40," and "x out."

One of Reagle's favorite puzzles is his "United Nations" crossword in which the themed answers were the names of two countries, which, when read together, formed a punny punchline:

Doc, I've got a —— in my neck!	Syria Spain
A lovely couple no doubt	Chad Andorra
—— right over? We're shorthanded	Kenya Senegal
Why don't —— out of the army?	Jamaica Korea
At Plumpy's our huge portions never	Libya Hungary
Flat tire eh? Your wife ain't ——	Ghana Bolivia

In "Auto-Suggestion" Reagle clued car models in an unusual manner:

Caught sight of a Mercury?	Spotted lynx
Arrived at a Honda?	Reached an accord
Honda owner's feeling?	Civic pride
Dodge for Christmas?	Omni present
Prepare to fix a VW's flat?	Jack rabbit

In "Double Play" he used double numerals in the themed answers:

Nick of time	11th hour
Like many Saturday night specials	22 caliber
LP speed	33⅓ rpm
Dirty Harry's "equalizer"	44 magnum
Sign of the times	Speed limit 55 mph
Maharis-Milner TV classic	Route 66
All-star disaster epic	Airport 77
Grand total?	88 keys
Smart partner	Agent 99

Reagle is one of the few constructors who can tell a story with his crosswords. In "A Night at the Movies" the thematic entries were all the "names of movies that sounded like you would have the worst night of your life at the theater." These included: *House of Usher, Wait Until Dark, Torn Curtain, The Big Chill, The*

Stranger, On Your Toes, The Wild Child, and *Dark Passage.*

In "Signs of Destruction" Reagle wrote another mini-screenplay. Each themed entry was clued as "sign in a department store that you hope Junior won't take literally." Among them:

Throw rugs
Pound cake
Slit skirts
Scatter pins
Pocket calculators
Watch repairs
Paint counter
Floor manager
Stretch socks

Unfortunately, Reagle lost out on winning first prize in the Bantam Great Master Contest because he had sent this puzzle to Dell Publishing Company and they told him that they were "putting it on hold." Reagle interpreted that as a rejection and sent the puzzle to Bantam without requesting its return from Dell. In the interim, Dell published the puzzle and thus made it ineligible for the prize.

Although Reagle lost out on the prize money, he did discover that editors were now paying more money for crosswords and he could afford to devote all of his time to puzzles. He is now one of the very few constructors who earns all of his income from creating crosswords. Unlike many of the other constructors profiled here, Reagle doesn't do any crossword editing. His puzzles appear in the *San Francisco Examiner, Games,* Dell Publications, *Detroit Monthly,* and numerous contests. In addition, he wrote *Sit and Solve,* a book of five-minute crosswords meant to be solved in the bathroom.

Reagle keeps in touch with editors and other constructors through lengthly telephone conversations. Reagle will call anyone at anytime and speak for hours. To make sure he never misses a call, he uses a telephone-answering machine answered by Reagle impersonating a celebrity.

In May 1986 Reagle became a writer for the revival version of *The Cross-Wits* TV show. The original show ran in the mid-seventies. Two three-member teams compete against each other by solving a Criss-Cross type of puzzle in which all the clues and answers relate to an overall topic. Each team is composed of two celebrities and one noncelebrity. Reagle writes the clues, which "tend to be kind of funny," e.g., "This Chevy is always crashing into things" for "Chase," and "When Rip Van Winkle woke up he had a real long one" for "beard."

Reagle acquired another puzzle-related job in the spring of 1986—solving the crosswords in the *Los Angeles Times* for a telephone service that helped solvers obtain the answers to this crossword puzzle.

The service was the brainchild of the Carina Group, a Los Angeles-based public-relations firm. The group devised an "interactive telephone call-in service" that provided answers to the Sunday *Los Angeles Times* crossword puzzle. Solvers called a special number and, by pressing the appropriate buttons on their telephones, received the answers to those clues, e.g., press 5 D for the answer to 5 Down. This service was based on "audiotex, a two-way communication with a computer where the caller receives an audio response through the telephone."

Doing his part of the job, Reagle, Marie Haley (his fiancée), and Martita Cooper (a friend) bought three copies of the *L.A. Times* on Saturday mornings, went to a restaurant, and solved the Sunday puzzle over breakfast. They brought a dictionary along and checked their answers with each other. The Carina representative met them, picked up the completed puzzle and took it to the office, where someone else read it into the computer in preparation for the answering service. Reagle and his teammates were reimbursed for all their expenses and, in addition, received a solving fee.

This service was discontinued after six months, but the Carina Group hopes to revive it and offer solutions to different local and national puzzles.

Totally immersed in the puzzle world, Reagle coordinated the first Great Western Crossword Puzzle Tournament in 1985. It drew fifty entrants to the Hyatt Hotel in Los Angeles to compete in a two-day solving bout. The first, second, and third place winners were Stanley Newman, Ellen Ripstein, and Richard Goodale, respectively. Newman breezed through the playoff puzzle, a joint effort by Reagle and Scott Marley, in a mere seven and a half minutes. He chuckled as he answered clues like "Salieri's tormentor, initially" (answered by "WAM," the initials of Wolfgang

Flyer for The Great Western Crossword Puzzle Tournament, coordinated by Merl Reagle

Amadeus Mozart); and "Where the blissful walk" (answered by "on air").

Reagle is one of the leaders of new-wave crosswords, defined by him as "a general movement toward more vitality and wit in crossword puzzles. It is a direct reaction to the straight conservative approach." Reagle's term for clues with question marks (?) is "teasers." The question mark tells the solver that the answer is funny or unexpected and should not be taken literally. Examples of Reagle's "teasers" include:

Refraining from McEnroeisms?	On one's best behavior
Buss boy?	Eros
Dirt collector?	Ear
Big game?	Super Bowl XX

Another type of new-wave clue is "one that is so stripped down that one must get one's bearings before solving it." For example, when a solver sees the clue "Charlie's bro," which is answered by "Syd," he or she must first figure out that "Charlie" refers to "Charlie Chaplin," then must recognize that "bro" is an abbreviation of "brother," and indicates an abbreviated answer—"Syd" instead of "Sydney." Reagle prefers to use clues like these "sparingly."

Reagle believes that "New Wavers like to be entertaining first, educational second, and challenging last. . . . Farrar always said that solvers want something fun and lively and entertaining, something to give their mind a little tweak."

SAINTS ALIVE! by Merl Reagle

(SEE PAGE 265 FOR SOLUTION)

ACROSS

1 Security investment
6 It means "eaters"
11 Oman man
15 —— turning point
18 "Day Is Done" singers
21 H_2O or CO_2, e.g.
22 Shuffled debts
24 Clothes moths
25 Pale potables
26 Wallop
27 Yegg's scheme
28 Rocky high points
30 Six ways —— (completely): slang
31 "—— everybody?"
32 Tethys, Titan, et al.
34 Girder
36 Stenerud and Sterling
37 Sault —— Marie
38 Southern Plains Indian
39 Up to this point
40 Mideast robe
42 He painted *The Garden of Love*
49 With eyes fixed
52 Caption
53 Believe everything
54 Yuri's predecessor
55 Decline
56 *Bier* ingredient
57 *Catch-22* character who "made it"
58 Outcropping
59 Anagram of this puzzle's theme words
61 All-purpose card
62 1970 Jackson 5 hit
63 Totally
65 Didymous entities
66 Spanish or spinach dish
68 Figurative fog
70 Washout
71 Moles
72 Popular sweet
75 "Come Back When You Grow Up" singer
76 Guy from Mattel
77 Tarzan transit
78 Fury
81 Editor's aside
84 Burgundies
85 Grab
86 Jack's dull without it
87 Cool shoes
90 Cithara-like instrument
91 "Oh give me —— . . ."
92 Game played in 17 Down
93 Wag's parry
95 Famous last words
97 Certain band member's froufrou
101 Waterman's prop
102 Jeff, on "The Donna Reed Show"
103 Sugar ending
104 Espionage series
105 Expensive Drive
106 Ladies of Spain

DOWN

1 "Thou art —— for ever" (Psa.)
2 Like Elsa
3 Optimally
4 Chomped twice
5 Wilbur Post's pal
6 Polish news agcy.
7 Shade
8 Wedding settings
9 Ossian's countrymen
10 Concerning
11 Part of a well-known Latin trio?
12 Any bird of prey
13 Sandarac trees
14 "How's ——?"
15 Mr. Spock's mom
16 Froot Loops flyer
17 Strike paths, perhaps
19 Workplaces for desk sgts.
20 Pre-AA affliction
23 Ranjit Singh was one
24 What you're reading
28 Matching dryers?
29 Rampaging
30 Giant armadillo
32 Stuck
33 Hamlin's caveman
34 Pat Collins' forte
35 Droplet
38 Soprano —— te Kanawa
40 C Asia sea
41 Nixon's agriculture secretary
42 Perfectly reasonable
43 Memphis residents
44 Act of continuing
45 True, to a Scot
46 French star
47 Playtex bestseller
48 Mother Goose couple
49 Abner's creator
50 Navy builder
51 Officer Dibble's nemesis
56 Insulation material
59 Young un's overseer
60 Expose
61 *Très, en anglais*
63 Driver's warning?

4 Actress Velez
6 —— *d'art*
7 Dairy sounds
9 Happy hour's end, often
0 Hightailed it
3 Luau strings
4 Watson and Crick "cracked" it
8 Newman hit
9 Monument-obsessed king
80 Ogling type
81 "—— shabby"
82 Gluck and Glinka works
83 Permanent job status
84 Get one's wind
85 Did business à la Bilko
86 Quantum theory unit
88 Rod's co-star in *The Birds*
89 Great grades
90 Try fooling
91 The Jetsons' dog
93 Chess pce.
94 Regular buyer
95 —— d'Oleron, France
96 Mind
98 Screen's Doc Savage
99 Start of many questions
100 It often offers Hope

MEL ROSEN

THE FIRST CROSSWORD puzzle Mel Rosen constructed was based on punny phrases: "monkey wench" was clued as "saucy prioress" and "stewed prudes" as "WCTU'ers in error." This Sunday-sized crossword was rejected by Will Weng at the *Times* because Rosen had exceeded the word-count limit and used a few "forced entries." However, Rosen took Weng's advice to "try again," and soon afterward saw his first crossword, a diagramless, printed in the *Times*.

That was in the late sixties. Since then Rosen has sold hundreds of crosswords and is now editing the highly successful Crossword Series for Running Press. Sales for all these books exceed 100,000 copies.

The story behind Rosen's appointment as editor is based on a rejected puzzle. In the late seventies Rosen sent a Tolkien-themed puzzle to Eugene Maleska, who returned it because he felt that the subject matter was too narrow for his broad-based audience. However, Maleska remembered Rosen and the puzzle when Running Press asked him to recommend a constructor for *The Tolkien Scrapbook*. The publisher contacted Rosen for this project initially and again two years later when it started its crossword series.

Rosen has been editing two crossword books a year since 1983, shifting gears easily from constructing to editing. He still constructs puzzles for *Games* magazine, Dell Publications, and his own books, but the constraints of a full-time job (he's a computer analyst) and the editorial responsibilities cut deeply into his constructing time.

Rosen recruited constructors for his first collection by culling names from a directory compiled by the Reverend Edward J. O'Brien, a crossword constructor who was inspired "to put crossword people in capacity to contact each other." Through the years his book has been used by many editors and constructors. Father O'Brien is also credited with coining the word "cruciverbalist," derived from the Latin word *crux* and *verbum,* meaning "cross" and "word".

When Rosen asked Margaret Farrar to update the addresses for him, she not only obliged but added fifteen to twenty names to his list. After the first book was published, other constructors sent unsolicited puzzles to Rosen and he now has a steady supply of contributors.

Rosen spends five to six months on each book and takes time off between projects. His wife, Peggy, helps him by "adding weight" to his "tentative decision to accept or reject puzzles" and by "wordsmithing a clue," i.e., spicing it up. She recently started to construct her own puzzles, and sold the first one to Rosen.

The Rosens live in Florida, where they both work for IBM. They're in their mid-forties and are the parents of two grown daughters.

Rosen used his computer skills to write a crossword program that replaces "graph paper and eraser crumbs." With the program Rosen can produce a blank grid that "manages the symmetry and placement of black squares, places the numbers in the solving grid, fills in an answer diagram, and prepares a properly numbered list of answers." After all this is completed, Rosen types in the definitions.

Rosen built a word-finder reference aid into the program. He bought a disk that contained all the words and phrases in both *The Official Scrabble Player's Dictionary* and the second edition of *Webster's New International Dictionary*. If he needs a specific word for a spot in the grid, e.g., a five-letter word whose second and third letters are N and J, he punches that information into the computer and the available words are spewed out.

Constructors without access to such a sophisticated program make extensive use of reference books like Funk and Wagnall's *Crossword Puzzle Word Finder,* which lists words according to letter patterns; e.g., to locate a six-letter word whose second and third letters are S and Y, one would look under - S Y - - - and find "asylum," "psyche," and "psycho."

Rosen's interest in puzzles began when he was six years old, putting letters into skeleton or criss-cross types of grids (those presented with just a blank diagram and a list of words to be placed inside). He graduated to crosswords a few years later. He credits his father with encouraging his crossword habit and dedicated his book, *The Compleat Cruciverbalist,* to him.

The verbal Rosen is exceptionally witty and, by his own admission, "fast with the mouth." When he gets together with other constructors, most notably Henry Hook, the two engage in such fast-paced repartee that they could regale a sit-com audience for hours. So it's natural for Rosen to use clever clues and witty themes in his puzzles. In "One Out" the trick was a deleted letter:

Pawn's plaint?	I am not a rook
Small claims courts?	Suer markets
Half-remembered singing duo?	Sonny and Her
Andrew Johnson's 1861 White House toast?	You and Me Abe
Calling Reagan a Conservative?	Branding Ron

In "Letter Trick" Rosen substituted letters for their homophones:

Revelation	I opener
North Sea inlet	Zuider Z
Ospreys	C eagles
Kitchen items	T spoons
Legendary kingdom of riches	L Dorado
Kansan	J Hawker

Rosen didn't use tricky wordplay in "Economy of Scales," but he did weave together diverse definitions for "majors" and "minors":

Military brass	Major generals
Most of Turkey	Asia Minor
Language specialist, in college	German major
The Dog Star	Canis major
Farm teams' locale	Minor leagues

In "What a Racket!" it's a tennis theme:

Public tennis area?	The People's Court
Avoid a double fault?	Serve one right
Quick tennis victory?	Four aces
Place for stowing rackets on a plane?	Overhead storage
Nobody scores?	Love conquers all

Unlucky sets?	Three on a match
Keeps one's opponent waiting?	Strings one along

Rosen gets his ideas from everyday life—catch phrases on TV, bits of conversation, newspaper items. He even gets ideas for new puzzles while checking facts on a puzzle he's editing. For example, while browsing through *Reader's Encyclopedia* he stumbled across a list of entries on "Fathers," e.g., "Father of Greek Prose," "Father of History," and created a puzzle called "Patrician Assembly."

Rosen is also adept at creating Puns and Twists, a variation of Puns and Anagrams. Examples of his clues for this genre include:

Ohio k'eventides	Knights of Columbus
Passedthefinishline	Ran on
Pfortune	Pluck
Road where wise men live?	Sagest

Many of his clues are in the new-wave genre:

Take out order	Dele
Make amends	Edit
Dentist's office	Filling station
Enjoy "Late Night with David Ladderman"	Elope
"We make coffee the old-fashioned way—we —— it!"	Urn

Rosen's hectic schedule leaves him little time for solving, but he can whiz through a 15 × 15 in three to eight minutes. He entered one crossword contest, at the first Grossinger's Crossword Weekend, and won second prize.

He has constructed crosswords for tournaments, his most notable one being "Position Wanted" for the 1986 Presenting Baltimore First Annual Crossword Open. This was the one in which words were put in the grid in literal relationships to each other—"Head" over "Heels," "Look" under "The Bed."

Stan Newman (see page 128), coordinator of the Baltimore event, wrote that "Gimmicks of the sort used in this puzzle work best when there is a blurb on top of the puzzle providing an appropriate warning, and an explanation of the gimmick with the solution (for solvers who didn't get it)."

In *The Compleat Cruciverbalist* Rosen and co-author Stan Kurzban (see page 82) include several chapters on how to solve crosswords. In their section "There Must Be a Catch to It!" they discuss the two main types of gimmicks—substitutions and rebuses. In the substitutions, "one word in the 'natural' answer has been replaced by another word. The switched words have some connections." A puzzle titled "Inflation" involves numbers, such as "six and eleven cent store."

In rebus-type gimmicks "a word or group of letters in the 'natural answer' has been replaced by a shape or drawing." In "Winning a Gold One" the letters "star" were replaced by *, forming expressions like "no *ch in my collar please."

Rosen and Kurzban advise solvers of gimmicky puzzles to gather their wits. "The composer of the puzzle is trying to rattle you. Think about the title of the puzzle: what relationship might it have to the gimmick? What about the timing of the puzzle? The *Times* commemorates many events and holidays throughout the year with apt thematic puzzles. Do your hypothetical answers seem proper for some occasion or national holiday? Is there some part of the answer that lends itself to a rebus or substitution? A title like 'By the Numbers' should suffice to 4warn you."

Rosen and Kurzban have a delightful section on the games experts play to make their solving a bit more challenging. These include: using pen instead of pencil (of course!); working only from the Down definitions (and using the Across definitions to verify answers); writing in only the *e*'s in the answer; and solving the puzzle mentally, that is, without bothering to fill in the grid.

Rosen doesn't solve cryptics mentally, but learned how to solve them in 1965 through trial and error, and taking an "infinite" amount of time to complete a diagram. In the late seventies Rosen won third prize in the Bantam Great Masters Crossword Puzzle Hunt for his cryptic crossword.

Rosen has been selling his crosswords and books for twenty years and has seen a lot of changes in solvers and constructors. He feels that solvers are "hipper" and more accepting of punny crosswords and feels that there are now more markets available to constructors in which to sell their products.

He is especially happy with his editorial responsibilities for the Running Press series and enjoys counseling new constructors and introducing their work. He remembers the words of praise and encouragement he received from both Margaret Farrar and Will Weng when he was starting out and is passing that tradition of treatment along to new constructors.

Rosen has very fond memories of Margaret Farrar's Golden Anniversary celebration in 1974. "I had an opportunity to meet her, Dr. Maleska, and so many other of the cruciverbalists. It's an introvert's hobby, at heart, but the participants are so witty that get-togethers are wonderful."

BRIEF ENCOUNTERS by Mel Rosen

(SEE PAGE 265 FOR SOLUTION)

ACROSS

1 Ready, willing and able
5 Tech. paper intro
8 Treasure
13 Followed by next entry, circus walkway
17 See previous clue
18 Outrage
19 Out of commission
20 Cotton tufts
21 Brief
23 Shark's symbiotic sidekick
24 Doctor's bane?
25 Simple answer
26 Annual publication
28 San Francisco Hill
29 Break 55
30 See 27 Down
32 Birds with bright plumage
34 "No Frills" Freddy
36 Fashion silhouette
38 Maximilian Schell's mini-series role
39 Buttons
40 "No ——," Roberto Duran's surrender
43 Ear area
44 Signal first used by the *Titanic*
45 Beauty salon treatment
47 Vacation house design
50 Throb
52 Thingamajig
53 Bacchante
54 Jeanne, e.g.
55 Allegro or largo
57 One crust
59 Attila's brother
60 Diamond official
61 Discoverer and mapper of the Roman catacombs
63 Footlike part
65 Privy to
66 Brief
70 Brief
73 Barbecue goodies
74 Western St.
75 Sling mud
77 Participate, prandially speaking
78 Like waves of grain
80 Remain still, at sea
82 Oscar nominees
84 Historical time
87 Entangled state
89 Soak through
91 Virginia ——
93 European turbot
94 Mr. Fudd
95 Wall Street order
96 Not on Mr. Blackwell's list
97 More than a few, in brief
98 *Pygmalion* author, in brief
100 Part of the Ankara skyline
102 Outbuildings
103 Work shirker
106 Worthy of painting
107 Good times
108 Spread out gradually
110 Latin I word
112 Spot —— (dog catcher?)
114 Roof finial
117 Head toward the wee hours
118 Salesman
120 Brief
122 "I will build me ——" (Lanier)
123 Hateful
124 Sooner than
125 Hardy cabbage
126 Uses a hitching post?
127 Religious groups
128 "My Gal ——"
129 "It's all downhill from here" device

DOWN

1 Off
2 Hollywood crossing
3 Brief
4 Andrea —— Sarto
5 Bridal path
6 Hat projection
7 Opening words at the cave?
8 Brief
9 Home computer storage, in brief
10 Religious images
11 Nothing
12 Permit
13 Winner of more than 50 world billiard championships
14 Brief
15 Strong breeze
16 Attention
19 Temporary laborer from Mexico
20 Wine storage
22 New Haven campus
27 See 30 Across
31 Change for a five
33 Trachea
35 Speaker of the first palindrome?
36 Ski heaven
37 Boorish character
38 "Ozymandias" or "Il Penseroso"
39 Kick out again
41 Punk; tinder
42 Family cars
44 Enter briefly
46 Fall guy
48 "The —— Four," the Beatles
49 Persistent remnant
51 Pressure meas.
52 Entryway
56 Caters
58 Musical notes
60 Oust
62 Pervasive
64 Inventor of the gyro-compass
66 Rail riders
67 Like oak bark

68 Brief
69 Part of AT&T
71 Hasty
72 Comfort
76 Brief
79 Q-U connection
81 —— -könig
83 —— above the rest (marginally better)
84 Brief
85 Tim ——, played Venus Flytrap on *WKRP in Cincinnati*
86 Searchlights
88 Poultry seasoning
90 Rubbernecks
92 Instant replay
95 Turns into
99 Cheers
101 Grand Canyon locale
102 Uncomfortable
104 Kind of code
105 Imparted
106 One of 107 Across
107 Asiatic palm
108 Shortcoming
109 Driving path
111 "One man's —— is another man's Persian."
113 Vague actress?
115 Carpet quality
116 Cooled down
119 Dash's partner
121 Endorses, briefly

JOHN SAMSON

JOHN SAMSON'S FIRST crossword, which he sent to Eugene T. Maleska at the *Times,* was so crude—it had two-letter words, a nonsymmetrical diagram and contrived phrases like "ox morgue"—that it was rejected immediately. But, along with the rejection, Maleska sent his standard guideline sheet and told Samson to study the *Times* puzzles.

Samson did his studying so well that he's now Maleska's assistant in many of his projects. The metamorphosis from tyro to professional evolved gradually as Samson did his homework. He analyzed the crosswords in the *Times* and Simon & Schuster books, constructed puzzles, revised them according to Maleska's suggestions, and resubmitted them. Finally, his first puzzle (a cooperative effort with a friend, David Pohl) was accepted by Maleska. Samson remembers the feeling of elation he had when he got that first acceptance. "Finally, we cracked through!"

Samson now derives all of his income from puzzle-related activities. He works out of an office near his home in Vernon, New York. He's very much the family man, devoted to his wife and two young children. He's a sensitive, creative person who is red-haired, slim, and youthful-looking. With Maleska, he edits the three Simon & Schuster books published yearly; he does all the editing and blurb writing for half the puzzles in each book. He also constructs puzzles for Dell, *Dun & Bradstreet Reports,* Home Box Office's monthly in-house magazine, and *Globe,* the tabloid newspaper. The latter, with its 35×35 grid, is billed as "the world's largest crossword." When this mammoth puzzle was replaced by a smaller version in one issue, so many readers protested this change that the editors quickly returned to the original format. Every few months *Globe* will publish a fan letter from a crossword aficionado. One solver wrote: "I love your crossword puzzle. It not only helps increase one's wordpower, but is also visually satisfying."

Samson received a lot of his constructing commissions from Maleska, whom Samson describes as "my mentor." Once Maleska saw Samson's talent he worked with him to bring out the best in him, guided him to other puzzle markets, and, after Margaret Farrar's death, hired him as co-editor on the Simon & Schuster series.

Samson's previous jobs were far removed from the crossword world. He wrote newspaper advertisements, published a book of poetry, *A Somber Night in June,* called in the results at a harness race track, sold vacuum cleaners, and painted portraits. He's been in the puzzle "business" since 1979.

Samson's first *Times* puzzle appeared in the March 18, 1979, issue and was co-authored by David Pohl, the friend with whom he often solved crosswords. The theme was "Expansion Teams":

New York debating team	Brooklyn accents
Leg-pulling Welsh team	Cardiff giants
Scrambling Russian team	Red alerts
Henley regatta team	Bath salts
Scottish phys. ed. team noted for coolness	Ayr conditioners
Emotional French team	Brest beaters
Middle Eastern ecdysiast team	Gaza strippers

Samson and Pohl collaborated on one more *Times* crossword, "Electricks," in which the definitions and/or entries related to electricity:

High tension area	Washington, D.C.
Tourist's togs	Bermuda shorts
Vivid hue	Shocking pink
Blotter entry	Assault and battery

Pohl has since died, but Samson continued to construct on his own.

His themes range from factual topics to gimmicky tricks. He starts with a theme idea and compiles a long list of theme entries—"the longer the list the better." His puzzles, which reflect a lot of research, are clued straightforwardly. Solvers enjoy a mental workout with a Samson puzzle but aren't bogged down with lots of "crosswordese." His puzzles can be solved in a fair amount of time.

In his "Inventions" crossword, he packed numerous inventions into a 21×21 grid. All were clued with the name of the inventor, e.g., "Hilliard invention" for "circuit breaker," "Joseph P. Friedman invention" for "flexible straw." Solvers could discover these inventions without any difficulty for the crossings were extremely fair.

For "Relatively Speaking," he researched the familial relationships between famous folks and used these entries and clues in the puzzle—"Brother of Peter Graves" for James Arness; "Arturo Toscanini's son-in-law" for Vladimir Horowitz; and "Barbara Hutton's cousin" for Dina Merrill.

In "Figure It Out" his diagram was "crammed with a remarkable number of meaningful numbers"—thirty-two ("number shared by Brown, Simpson, and Harris of football fame"); seventy-six ("spirit of ——, presidential plane"); forty-niner ("he went west"); fifteen ("hurling team").

The crosswords that Samson creates for specialized magazines always relate to the publication in which they appear. Thus the puzzles for *HBO* always have a movie theme, while the ones for *D & B Reports* are business-oriented. Examples of the latter:

Like some indolent employees	Last in first out
Rein for Robert E. Lee's horse?	Traveler's check
Amortization on the *Titanic?*	Sinking fund
Two Chicago teams	Bulls and Bears

In "Initial Drop" Samson's theme entries were the names of famous personalities with the first letter of their last name removed. The personalities were then clued with references to their "new" names:

English songbird	Petula Lark
Actress who deserved her Emmy	Michael Earned
Designer with a young lady in mind	Bill Lass
Nast uprooted him	Boss Weed

Samson is "always looking for new ways to clue old words":

They loop the Loop	Els
Jump house to a spouse?	Elope
VIP at VPI	Dean
Sesame Street resident	Elmo
They keep others awake	Snorers

He learned about "Elmo" from his two-and-a-half-year-old daughter who regularly watches *Sesame Street*.

John Samson created a crossword for the rock group Blotto, which was used on the group's album cover.

Samson's puzzles have appeared in two places where crosswords are rarely found—on a record cover and in a book of quilt designs. He was commissioned to create a crossword for the rock group Blotto. The puzzle appeared on an album cover—the diagram covered the front of the album while the clues were on the back cover. The grids that Samson uses in his puzzles for *Globe* appeared in a book on quilt designs. A solver liked his patterns so much that she asked him for permission to include them in her quilting book. He readily agreed.

Eugene Maleska included Samson's "Turnabout" crossword in *Across and Down*. In this puzzle, Samson's entries were typical crossword definitions, while the clues were typical crossword answers:

Hemp	Rope fiber
1051	MLI, to Caesar
Alan	Actor Alda

"Turnabout" is also an appropriate way to describe the route John Samson traveled from a dilettante who dashed off a throwaway crossword to a top constructor whose work appears in all the major publications.

TYPECASTING by John Samson

(SEE PAGE 265 FOR SOLUTION)

ACROSS

1 Roster
5 Delight
10 Senegal capital
15 David or Swampy
19 Image
20 Phar Lap in *Phar Lap*
21 —— François Loubet
22 Farrago
23 Film starring Dapper Dan?
25 Film starring Fatty Arbuckle?
27 Assaults
28 Roll cloud
30 Solarium
31 Sgt.
32 Suffix for correct
33 —— *Ballou*
34 Counts
38 Smokes
40 Kind of code
44 Court name
45 Stamp for a passbook
47 Mrs. Peel's partner
49 Ninth Arabic letter
50 Pack or pick preceder
51 Expert
52 Actress Reinking
53 Ratite of Canberra
54 Collars
56 Film starring Our Man Flint?
61 *Let* —— (Beatles film)
62 Gastronome
64 Singled out
65 Country in I Kings 10:22
67 Tabby, in Toledo
68 Scrap
69 Lucille's son
70 Label incorrectly
73 Wild stars of *Porky's*?
75 Dairycase items
78 Woes
79 Film starring Alberto Salazar?
82 Paradise lost
83 Born
84 Sutherland film, 1981
85 Maritime avian
86 Murray of silents
87 Catullus creations
89 Less aboveboard
91 Secretaries
93 Al- ——, Saudi oil region
94 Satiated
96 More dilatory
98 Osculated, in Chaplin's day
100 Indiana's governor
101 Society newcomer
102 MGM has two
103 Cheap cigars
107 Louise and Turner
109 Mad Hatter's hour
113 Film starring Edwin H. Land?
115 Film starring Cab Calloway?
117 Ollie's pal
118 Kline or Costner
119 Meritocracy
120 "Le Roi d'Ys" composer
121 Doesn't burn, in a sense
122 Foam
123 Refurbish the outfield
124 Montana's targets

DOWN

1 *Educating* ——, 1983 film
2 Folk singer Phil
3 Baby's "little piggies"
4 Faster than adagio
5 Tolkien's —— *of the Rings*
6 Diana who played Lady Day
7 Vetch
8 On the drink
9 Cairn or Skye
10 Shows up
11 General Halftrack
12 Gavilan or McCoy
13 Namesakes of a Khan
14 Abridged
15 Wooed
16 White: comb. form
17 Actor O'Shea
18 Epic
24 *Street Scene* playwright
26 —— even keel
29 Ovett's rival
34 "Dirigo" is its motto
35 Org. founded by Victor Herbert
36 Film starring Rip van Winkle?
37 Joan's role in *Rain*
38 Violin ancestor
39 Goggle
40 *The Balcony* dramatist
41 Film starring Abel?
42 Metrical feet
43 Puzzle parts
46 Gob
48 Tree in 5 Down
55 Thumbs through
56 *The Sane Society* author
57 Film a film
58 The Pentateuch
59 Star: comb. form
60 Noble gas
61 Upshot
63 Actress Hagen

66 Unleaded's bro.
70 Secondary
71 —— la Cité
72 American tall ship
73 City on the Rhine
74 Scoff
75 Jerks
76 Josh
77 The Masters winner, 1954
80 Man of art
81 —— *Soffel*, 1984 film
88 Shibboleths
89 Like a bad paint job
90 Refulgent
91 "Firing Line" guest
92 Zipped
93 Antagonistic
95 Stoltz in *Mask*
97 Film starring Madame X?
99 Sharif
103 Winnow
104 Hall in *GWTW*
105 Muscat locale
106 "Jolly Roger" crewman
107 Speaker of Cooperstown
108 Port of NW Morocco
109 Landrum of baseball
110 Bulgarian writer Vazov
111 Blend
112 Anteros' brother
114 Mrs. Jerome Kern
116 Greek letters

A. J. SANTORA

A MASTER CROSSWORD CONSTRUCTOR, A. J. Santora joins words in his grids just as solidly as he joins Sheetrock to build houses—his other construction business. The New England-based Santora uses the harsh winters that ruin his construction schedules to construct the sixty to one hundred puzzles he sells per year. These appear in most major puzzle publications including *The New York Times, Games* magazine, the Simon & Schuster books, *Dell Champion Crossword Puzzles,* Will Weng's *Crosswords Club,* the Running Press series, and *The Crossworder's Own Newsletter.*

Santora is tall, dark, and handsome and looks much younger than his sixty-seven years. He's soft-spoken, eager to please, and is always willing to send his puzzles to new publications in addition to maintaining his commitments to his regular outlets.

Unlike many other puzzle addicts, Santora didn't start solving crosswords until he was twenty-eight years old. He quickly turned to constructing and was one of the few people whose first published puzzle appeared in the *Times*. That was in 1948.

In addition to the $35.00 he received for that puzzle (it was a 23×23), he started to be known as A.J., rather than his given name. As Santora recalls, "Margaret Farrar edited everything in that first puzzle, including my name." Farrar had taken the initials from the mailing envelope and used them on the by-line, much to Santora's pleasure. He always hated his given name (which he won't reveal) and he's been known as A.J. ever since.

Santora's wife, Rose, is actively involved in this construction career. She helps him with theme ideas, proofreads his puzzles, suggests appropriate publications for submissions, and exercises her veto power when Santora "strays a bit" with way-out themes or clues.

Santora's work is hard to categorize for he's a jack of all trades and master of many. His "West Undies" puzzle for the 1981 Stamford contest was based on a "quote by Mae West on learning a life jacket was named for her." Santora was able to fit all this—

"I've been in *Who's Who* and I know what's what but it's the first time I ever made the dictionary"—into a 17 × 17 grid.

Santora can pack more thematic entries into his diagrams than most people. His "In the Beginning" crossword for one of Margart Farrar's calendar series spotlighted "the people who started it all"—Adam and Eve. His eight theme entries included:

Familiar couple	Adam and Eve
Features of necks	Adam's apples
Lively comic on TV	Steve Martin
Work on the road	Macadamize
"The —— had drunk his fill"	Stag at eve
Pitcher plants	Eve's cups
Alias "Our Miss Brooks"	Eve Arden
Evening in Evesham	Levelling

Santora's themes cover a wide range of topics—entertainers, films, sports, marriage, colors—and are solidly constructed with a minimum amount of esoterica and a maximum amount of literate phrasing.

His ability to join words in a diagram is best exemplified by two of his all-time classics. "Locus-Pocus" originally appeared in the *Times* in 1977 and was highly rated by Eugene T. Maleska and other top constructors. Santora juxtaposed phrases and words in a totally original way. For example, "below normal" appeared in the grid on the line below the word "normal"; "by the hour" appeared vertically next to "hour"; "aboveboard" was positioned on top of "board."

His "Squarely Figured" crossword was reprinted in Eugene T. Maleska's *Across and Down*. Santora filled this diagram with numerals that matched their corresponding numbers in the grid, e.g., the answer to "New York street" was "East 40th" with the 40 appearing in the square of the same number. Similarly, "Where 126 is" was answered by "after 125" with the numeral fitting into the box number 125 and crossing with "Impost at Aqueduct" answered by "125 pounds."

Most of the letters that Santora has received from fans have been complimentary. However, one fan composed a poem in quasi-Italian language complaining that his puzzles "were too tougha" and urged Santora to ease up "or his wife would get a divorca."

Just as Santora meticulously follows different blueprints when building houses, he never uses the same patterns when building crosswords. He "likes to take long entries from fifteen to twenty-one letters and put two or three of these in juxtapositon while letting the pattern form itself around these words."

For his "Center Stage" crossword based on Shirley MacLaine, Santora positioned three thematic entries in an unusual manner in the center of the grid:

B E I N G T H E R E
T W O F O R T H E S E E S A W
O U T O N A L I M B

Santora's clues don't follow patterns either:

Get to the bottom	Spank
Put on hold	Wrestle
Thinks nothing of	Gets off one's mind
Trek stops?	Asteroids
TV movie	Cassette
Mr. Rose's well-being?	Pete's sake
Torme thrillers?	Melodramas
Fiddler on the reef	Crab

Santora can pull together unrelated entries and combine them under a thematic umbrella, such as those in his "Metal Telepathy" puzzle. Solvers had to "dig for" these answers:

Attributes of gourmands?	Cast iron stomachs
Pittsburgh brass?	Steelheads
Midas's pinkie?	Goldfinger
A deposit in the reservation?	Indian head nickel
"Bleacherite" with the metallic look?	Platinum blonde
Hippie's house decor?	Aluminum siding

Sometimes Santora's themes are more subtle. In his "On Approval" crossword the theme entries all contained the letters O.K.:

Know like ——	A book
Southern swamp	Okefenokee
Gains approval	Gets the O.K.
"Wild" one of the Old West	Bill Hickok
Best-selling self-help book	I'm O.K., You're O.K.

Locale for a gunfight	The O.K. Corral
Van Buren's sanctions org.	The O.K. Club

In his "In Things" crossword, clues and definitions related to various interpretations of "in":

Afflicted with an indoor psychosis	Stir crazy
Fogy	Stick-in-the-mud
In-dwelling ailment	Cabin fever
Indoors-man	Stay at home
In-residence confinement	House arrest

Santora is an avid sports fan and uses sporty clues whenever possible. For his "Sports Calendar" crossword he assembled "Timely sports figures" such as: "Mr. October" ("Reggie Jackson at Series time"); Don January ("A golfer for all seasons!"); Rudy May ("Sometime Yankee pitcher"); Bill Summers ("One-time American League umpire"); and Rick Monday ("Sometime Dodger slugger").

Santora is truly a person who has been able to manage two different careers successfully. Although the number of people who can buy a building constructed by A. J. Santora is limited, millions can derive pleasure from his crossword constructions.

I.Q. TEST by A. J. Santora

(SEE PAGE 266 FOR SOLUTION)

ACROSS

1 Baby talk
5 Davis and Stanley
9 Edict
13 "There ought to be ——!"
17 Cupid
18 "It's —— wind that . . ."
20 Tagging along
22 Henry of *Time*
23 Official pronouncement
25 The street, in Paris
26 Metrical foot
27 Lively
28 NHL team
31 *Atlas Shrugged* Rand
32 Profligate
34 Pep squad cheer
35 Premier Ismet in Turkey
36 Rid of wrinkles
39 "Do —— say, not . . ."
40 Bulgarian capital
44 Algonquian
46 Setdowns
48 Companies bidding
50 "You can't fire me, ——!"
51 Sta. workers
53 Skip
55 Afflicted
56 Frank
57 Music halls
58 The last in line
60 One —— million
61 Day of the month
63 Grape drink
65 Arrest
66 Kind of graph
67 Book —— (Horae)
69 Kind of body
71 Pavarotti no.
73 Zigzag
75 —— dime (veer sharply)
78 Annoy
79 Grown together
80 Silly
81 "Dragnet" actor
83 Troublemaker of myth
85 Flammable gas
87 Kind of metrics
88 The Pyramids
89 Golfer-announcer Ken
91 Rolls follower
93 Antique auto
94 —— Arantes do Nascimento (Pelé)
95 Math meas.
97 Weaklings
100 Man-sized load, in China
102 Equal
103 Her ——, Georgia Gibbs
104 Scotland's longest river
107 Good grace
112 Eland's kin
114 Wife of Zeus
115 Loud, in the stands
116 West Indies mecca
118 Dynamite guy
119 Whirly-birds?
120 Arab ruler
121 Gather
122 Kind of terrier
123 Thou —— (you do)
124 Father Marquette
125 Contained

DOWN

1 Capital of Bangladesh
2 Cleveland writer
3 Atlanta Hawks' star
4 Warfare
5 Preserve
6 Incomparable
7 Aroused
8 Skid sideways
9 Steal
10 "Love —— Automobile" (1899 song)
11 For three: French
12 First-aid device
13 Divides evenly
14 Feast
15 The very top
16 Networks
19 French president before WW II
21 "—— It" (1977 song)
24 Eradicate
29 Gulp down!
30 —— many words
33 Toronto's prov.
37 Kaput
38 Pelion pile-on
39 Assyrian worship
41 Friedan book
42 Singer Arkhipova
43 Make —— at (try)
44 Padre —— (Holy Father)
45 Athl. gear
47 Close-fitting bodice
49 Arriviste
51 The Flit
52 God
54 Mexicali breaks
57 Point ——
59 Part of USA
62 "—— Smile Be . . ."
63 Indicating "the mind"
64 Bo equals

68 Testimonial givers
70 ". . . . , It's off —— we go"
71 Holey cow!
72 Went wrong
74 Rembrandt's madder
76 Craft for E.T.
77 French curate
80 Per ——
82 Scouting org.
84 Strike
86 USSR border town
88 Univ. of Arizona campus
90 Unicorn fish
92 Lent at Notre Dame
93 Beknight
96 The Toledo bull
98 Chicken Kiev, e.g.
99 Non-eater
101 Auto or pluto ending
102 Alphabetic sequence
105 China shop charger
106 Productivity
107 —— ed. (gym class)
108 Fume
109 Binge
110 Writers Cameron and Fleming
111 Use the whacker
113 Fertile
117 Anger

ARTHUR SCHULMAN

AN ASSOCIATE PROFESSOR of psychology at the University of Virginia, Arthur Schulman looks at crosswords differently from most constructors. Because he knows a great deal about cognitive processes and has done research on memory, one of his concerns is to "discover the possibility of interlock and how words can be stacked."

Schulman, at fifty-two, has been a cognitive psychologist for twenty years. He uses his knowledge of problem solving, memory, imagery, minds, and machines (all the subjects he teaches to undergraduate and graduate students) when he constructs crosswords. He points out that constructors draw upon whole sets of words that will fit with words already in place. Moreover, he feels that "words that wouldn't fit into the diagram will not even come to mind. For example, if 'quartz' is the first word placed in a diagram, the constructor will immediately see the possibilities of using the word 'unsure' directly beneath it."

Schulman can construct a 15×15 diagram fairly rapidly, in thirty minutes or so. "The clues take the time, not the construction, which can take almost as little time as is required physically to enter the letters in the diagram," he notes. He uses no reference books for the construction itself. In fact, he does not own "a crossword puzzle dictionary or any other references that might help to fill in a diagram." He refers to the "usual dictionaries and encyclopedias for the clues, especially for proper nouns."

Crossword constructors usually have large libraries of reference books for they need a wide variety of sources for their clues. A typical crossword by any constructor can have references to art, literature, music, history, biology, chemistry, popular culture, film, etc. For solvers, this aspect of crosswords is what makes them so interesting for they can draw upon their whole range of knowledge while solving any given crossword on any given day.

Schulman's puzzles cannot be categorized in terms of themes. His crosswords tend to be very difficult for he's more concerned with the word interlock than entertainment. Solvers who enjoy excruciatingly hard mental workouts love his puzzles.

Schulman's puzzles that have appeared in Stan Newman's *Crossworder's Own Newsletter* and *Bull's-Eye Crosswords* will give some indication of the level of difficulty:

Self-destructive instinct	Thanatos
Dullness of mind	Hebetude
Trigger et al.	Palominos
About 3.26 light years	Parsec
Insect's thoracix plates	Scutella
Green turtles	Chelonia
Where the plot thickens	Epitasis
Hookworm, for instance	Hematode
Deity worshipped at Nineveh	Nisroch
Bowling ball brand	Ebonite
Napoleon's horse	Marengo
Hannibal's brother	Hasdrubal

On those rare occasions when Schulman does use a semantic theme, it will be a very loosely based one. His "Wise Cracks" puzzle for the ninth annual Stamford Marriott Tournament contained fourteen themed clues all with the word "break" in them:

Fracture	Bone break
Shaw play	*Heartbreak House*
Eruption	Outbreak
When early birds rise	At the break of day

Schulman's thematic puzzles differ from others of this genre because his theme words don't appear in the usual places. He doesn't regularly set out to do a themed puzzle, but when he does one such as "Wise Cracks" he concentrates on fitting as many thematic entries as possible into the diagram rather than fitting them into "traditional" positioning in the third or thirteenth horizontal rows, where they're usually found in a 15×15 diagram. Schulman had originally submitted the puzzle to Will Shortz for *Games,* but Shortz had hesitated to use it in his Pencilwise section because of its maverick placement of themed clues. Shortz opted to use it in a tournament instead.

Schulman's interest in puzzles began when he was about ten—he was inspired to solve crosswords by three of his uncles who were aficionados and whom he saw fairly regularly. He started to construct puzzles at about the same time, and sold his first crossword to Margaret Farrar at the *Times* when he was just sixteen. One day, shortly after his puzzle had been published, he took the subway from Brooklyn to Manhattan and walked, unannounced, into the editorial department of the *Times*. He introduced himself to Farrar, who was delighted to meet him. Schulman is clear about that first meeting. "Mrs. Farrar was in the middle of an enormous room. I couldn't imagine someone doing any editing in that atmosphere; nor could I understand how anyone could sit in those uncomfortable chairs."

Schulman had a warm and memorable relationship with Farrar for the rest of her life. She often told people that he was one of the top ten constructors of all time. She accepted every puzzle he sent her (between 1955 and 1965 he had more than one hundred puzzles in the *Times*) and rarely asked him to change anything. The two exceptions were the times he used Alexander Dubček's name in a puzzle and the time he used the word "bawd" in a diagram. About Dubček, the liberal Czechoslovakian Communist leader who was removed from office by the Soviet forces in 1969, Farrar's objection was that "solvers can get bad news from the front page of the newspaper; they shouldn't receive it on the puzzle page." And "bawd" was the type of word that Farrar would never permit in a puzzle; when she asked Schulman to rework that corner he did so.

The last letter Margaret Farrar dictated to her secretary before she died was addressed to Schulman. "Your timing is impeccable," she wrote. "You came along just in time . . . with two puzzles that I can use right away. You must keep a calendar as one of your scientific projects." She continued to praise "constructors of your brilliance," and thanked him "with all my heart" for the puzzles. She did not live to sign the letter.

Though Farrar had the highest regard for Schulman she didn't agree with him (or with many of her other constructors) about the special joys of solving cryptic crosswords. Farrar, according to Schulman, "never really understood cryptics." In fact, she mentioned to several constructors that she "couldn't see the point of them." Moreover, she felt that her solvers "weren't ready for them."

Schulman first became enamored of English cryptics when workers at *The New York Times* went on strike in 1964. Like most crossword solvers, he looked for crosswords in alternate publications and found them in *The New York Review of Books* and the Manchester *Guardian*. At first he "couldn't make sense of the clues for weeks at a time for there were no clues telling you how the game was played." And when he did answer the clues, half the words were unfamiliar to him because they were drawn from the Chambers dictionary. Schulman thinks solvers can master cryptics just by following the rules of assembly. Even if the answer words are unfamiliar, solvers know they're correct because they've followed the rules. Thus, in a cryptic clue that reads "Alert about start of business chain," the answer has to be "albert"—"alert" about "b" (start of business). American solvers might not know that an albert is a watch chain, but they will know that the clue is a container type and the answer has to be albert.

Schulman is interested in another aspect of English crosswords—use of the bar puzzles so prevalent in English newspapers and periodicals. He feels that bar puzzles enable constructors to use a whole different lineup of words. They "open up other possibilities that don't exist with squares."

According to Alec Robbins, author of *The ABC of Crosswords,* bar puzzles are "generally used for the more difficult kind of crosswords." This type "has an arrangement of 'bars' or thickened lines, instead of blocks . . . so that every single square of the diagram is used to accommodate a letter. The bars mark the end of each word in the diagram thus performing the same function as blocks."

Schulman feels that "there's no reason to use blocks and symmetry except for convention." While accepting the fact that crosswords "must have rules," he bends these rules when constructing puzzles for his family or friends.

Schulman constructed a specialized puzzle for the sixteen members of his squash group, the "Nickwits." The grid resembled a squash court and even included a serving line. By using a nonsymmetrical bar grid he was able to fit every player's surname into the diagram.

Schulman made up a puzzle for his daughter, Ruth, when she was seven years old. The answer words included colors—yellow, blue, green, red, etc. To help her along, he crayoned each color into its answer spot in the diagram. Thus, Ruth's realization that she could "solve" the puzzle through recognition of the colors

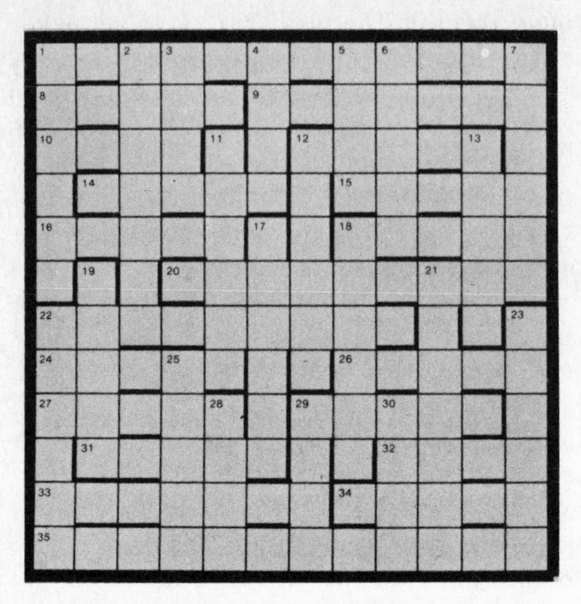

Diagram for a bar crossword

was a breakthrough of sorts, albeit a very elementary one. But her experience shows that it's "important for solvers to realize they can see a solution after first thinking that one is not possible."

In 1986 Schulman took a leave of absence from the University of Virginia and spent a semester at Amherst working on his forthcoming book, *The Mind of the Puzzler*. His *raison d'être* for the book, as expressed in his proposal, is to "examine the mind of the puzzler; how he approaches his problems, and how his solutions emerge. Fitting words into diagrams calls for unusual sensitivity to lexical structure, while devising misleading clues—especially for cryptic crosswords—requires special sensitivity to syntactic and semantic ambiguity." Schulman's intent is to "explore some of the cognitive implications of such heightened sensitivity to letters and language."

Schulman is as distinguished as his writing. He's a short man with graying hair, who looks like everybody's image of a professor. He exudes energy, talking rapidly and animatedly, especially about crosswords.

Crossworders' fascination with words is really the crux of all puzzle solving. Schulman's research into a puzzler's mind is reminiscent of F. Gregory Hartswick's introduction to the first crossword book: "The cross word solver becomes a collector, a connoisseur of words. They lose, to him, their mundane purpose of a suitable medium for the exchange of thoughts, and take on an esoteric significance. . . . The solver's [words] twine and intertwine, each leading to others, resulting in a harmonious whole unapproached by any except the masterpieces of classic literature."

MISCELLANY by Arthur Schulman

(SEE PAGE 266 FOR SOLUTION)

ACROSS

1 Not done
10 Churchman
15 *Ninotchka* star
20 Tip
21 Pueblo near Albuquerque
22 Anesthetic
23 Tennessee's vehicle?
24 Town where GOP was born
25 Bikini
26 Common contraction
27 Korean GI
28 Writer's aid
30 Communication device
32 Galatea's lover
34 Not king-sized
36 In addition
37 Tripe is a specialty here
38 Kind
40 Roots, perhaps
41 Cordiality
43 On the border
45 Meadow
46 Theatrical vantage point
47 Wordsmith for Kurt Weill
51 Thatcher, et al.
53 Remote
55 Triumphant cry
56 In pieces
59 Beacon Hill neighbor
60 Hard conclusion?
61 —— General
62 In good fortune
63 Rigoletto's daughter
64 Up
65 Chowder mate
66 Endangered California species
67 Twelfth of a sequence
68 Teamster's work
69 Modern missile
70 Polanski heroine
71 Ashamed
72 Spouses, once
73 UN acronym
74 Get the point
75 Bed or bell predecessor
76 When work begins, for many
78 Baseball play
79 Cry's partner
80 Michelin and others
84 Except
86 Poznan, to a Berliner
88 Jet
89 *Laughing Cavalier* creator
92 Street name
93 Marranos, e.g.
95 Where Vega is
96 Disturb
98 Inclined plane
99 He calls strikes
101 Jazzman's nickname
102 Accepted
103 City on the Han and Yangtze
105 Matured
108 Happening
109 Edict
110 Valuable
111 Transmits
112 They can make waves
113 Chic

DOWN

1 Divert attention from
2 Saw
3 Game like field hockey
4 Cockney's present
5 Estuary in Brittany
6 Revolving part
7 AL Hall-of-Famer
8 —— *pro nobis*
9 Bushings
10 Pres. of Brazil in WW II
11 More slippery
12 Ancient Egyptian
13 I love, in Latin
14 Ill will
15 Reverse, e.g.
16 Case
17 Girl's name
18 Give a false impression
19 Modern fabric
29 Stewpot
31 Capital of Maharashtra
33 Grips
35 Cosmetic colloid
36 Subject to the IRS
39 Was contemptuous
41 In service
42 Rugby play
44 Raw
46 Support
48 Native of Ur
49 Poser
50 Painting, etc.
52 Common contraction
53 Side
54 Means
56 Gave a hand to
57 Amos Oz, e.g.
58 FDR cabinet member
59 Tenacious
60 It's a factor
62 Make fun of

63 Question for certain passengers
65 Place of refuge
66 Edward Gordon —— (English actor)
68 Panama, e.g.
69 Draw
71 Village
72 Fast
74 Presidential nickname
75 They may have done it
77 London district
79 Pennock's pitching teammate
81 Working mother's boon
82 Gets to see red
83 Certain bottoms
85 Enlarged
86 Fruit
87 New Caledonian port
89 Despises
90 Plant of the amaryllis family
91 Compare
93 Pit
94 Vilify
97 Colonists
98 Arctic fish
100 Job
104 Instrument, for short
106 Chair support
107 Games' partner

MIKE SHENK

In college, Mike Shenk would always try to find a seat in a lecture class behind someone who was solving a crossword in the school newspaper. It was "more interesting to watch people solving the puzzle than to pay attention to the lecture." Since Shenk constructed all the puzzles for the school newspaper he had a vested interest in how they were received.

Shenk started to solve puzzles when he was in junior high school. His mother often purchased mass-market puzzle magazines; after solving the crosswords she'd turn the magazine over to Shenk. He honed his solving skills on the small variety puzzles at the bottom of the pages and graduated to crosswords when he was in high school. By the time he was in college he was an avid solver.

Thus, when he overheard the new editor of the college newspaper discussing his desire for a regular crossword feature, Shenk put samples of his puzzles in this editor's mailbox. The editor was so pleased with Shenk's work that he opted to use his fellow student's puzzles instead of buying them from a syndicate.

Shenk recalls that when his crossword puzzles were first printed there were "a lot of eyebrow-raising entries." Shenk relied on "obscure abbreviations" and "lots of German words" to fill in the blanks. As he progressed through college his crosswords improved tremendously. As he notes, "I learned how to make crosswords in college."

Graduating from Penn State in 1979 with a major in math, Shenk embarked on a short-lived teaching career. He continued to supply the college newspaper with five puzzles a week, but had branched out to other markets. During this time Bantam launched its Great Masters Crossword Puzzle Hunt and Shenk submitted two entries, both of which were fourth-prize winners.

Flushed with this success, Shenk started to submit crosswords to Will Shortz at *Games*. Shortz accepted almost every puzzle Shenk sent in and asked Shenk for more information about himself. When Shenk mentioned that he was unemployed (he had resigned his less than satisfactory teaching job after one year), Shortz asked him to "drop in" to the *Games* office if he was ever "in the neighborhood" (a mere 150 miles away). Shenk made it a point to be in the neighborhood rather rapidly and met with Shortz and Mike Donner, who was then editor in chief. Over lunch, Shortz and Donner interviewed Shenk. A few months later they offered him a job as an assistant editor, which he readily accepted.

Shenk has been at *Games* ever since and now holds the title of associate editor. His official duties are editing the cryptic crosswords, word searches, small variety puzzles for the Pencilwise section, and all the puzzles for the Wild Cards section.

Wild Cards are any short puzzles that don't require pencil and paper to solve and run the gamut from word games to math puzzles. A typical column might contain a list of fairy tales disguised as fictitious headlines, e.g., REMOTE COUNTRY HOME VANDALIZED BY BLONDE for "Goldilocks and the Three Bears"; an exercise in matching up imaginary business names with their services or products, e.g., THE HITCHING POST with "wedding chapel" and SOLE BROTHERS with "shoe store"; and a trivia quiz on captains associated with pop culture, e.g., "Who would never have left port without eating breakfast?" (Answer: Cap'n Crunch, the cereal.)

Wild Card selections are supplied mainly by *Games* readers, though the staff will also submit original items for this column. Since supply always exceeds demand here, Shenk accepts only about one out of every ten Wild Card submissions.

Shenk is also in charge of the crossword acceptances and rejections. Since *Games* publishes fewer than fifty crosswords per year, Shenk can accept only those with something special about them. However, he gives constructive criticism to those people whose puzzles show a real flair and directs constructors of marketable crosswords to alternate publications via the puzzle network.

The network is a very unstructured organization of puzzle editors of mass-market magazines, book series, and syndicates. Many of these editors know each other through the National Puzzlers' League and puzzle tournaments. They keep in touch with each other on a regular basis and recommend constructors to one another and/or guide constructors to each other's publications.

Shenk's role at *Games* goes far beyond his "official" duties. Boyish-looking and slender, Shenk, now in his late twenties, is one of the new-wave constructors whom solvers most identify with creative cluing and innovative crosswords. Since he's been at *Games* he's introduced a variety of puzzles that are usually not found in any other publications.

"Marching Bands," a variation of an Italian puzzle, is quite popular with *Games* readers. Words in the puzzle march around the grid in two ways—across in rows and around the perimeter in bands. Each square is used exactly twice—once in a Row word and once in a Band word. Shenk's variation of the Italian version is to start the band at the top of the grid. This made the puzzle more difficult to construct, but Shenk likes this particular constraint, probably because it relates to his math background.

"Gridlock," another Shenk puzzle, has a minimum of black squares and three major areas of white squares. The top and bottom horizontals consist of three words of eleven, thirteen, and fifteen letters respectively, e.g.:

S P A C E C A D E T S
H O R S E R A D I S H E S
R E D U C E D S E N T E N C E

Shenk was motivated to construct Gridlock in an unusual way. When Shortz was researching material for his *World Class Championship Crosswords* book, he often went directly to the Forty-second Street Library after leaving *Games*. Shenk left with him one evening and they stopped first at a fast-food place. During their meal Shortz drew a gridlock diagram, mentioned that he had always liked this pattern, and planned to build a puzzle around it someday. Shortz then went off to the library and Shenk went home—where he whipped up the Gridlock puzzle overnight and presented it to Shortz the next day. Shortz was bowled over and has included it on a semi-regular basis in the Pencilwise section. Shenk felt that Shortz was challenging him with the Gridlock diagram and thus felt really motivated to meet that challenge.

Shenk contributes to the overall creativity so evident in the pages of *Games*. The working atmosphere is conducive to innovation—all staff members feel very free to bounce creative ideas off of each other. Innovation prevails over the tried and true.

Shenk's "Numbers Racket" crossword contained one incorrectly numbered clue (27 Across instead of 28 Across) and three undefined clues (62 Across, 99 Across, and 71 Down). These were answered respectively by: "Sorry wrong number," "Central figure," "Ninety-nine across," and "Out of order."

His "A-Plus" crossword was filled with words whose only vowel was the letter "A." His "Amazement" crossword was both a crossword and a maze. After completing the diagram in the usual way, solvers wound their way through the diagram, one square at a time, by traveling only through squares containing the letters in LABYRINTH.

Shenk's variety puzzles are clever too. In "Family Pictures," he presented drawings of eighteen diverse objects that solvers had to group into six "families" of three members each. Solvers had to determine the common element among the members, a fact that wasn't readily apparent. Thus, the family of "colors" was represented by a golf mound (green), a flower (violet), and a fruit (orange). Similarly, the "NFL teams" family was represented by two airplanes (Jets), a stack of receipts (Bills), and two Norse warriors (Vikings).

Shenk's puzzles and clues always force solvers to think along nontraditional lines. Some examples of his style:

Take into account	Deposit
Kind of shell	Taco
Tanner's wear	Bikini
Prop on the bench	Gavel
Source of drafts	Keg
Small Bills	Wms.
It's hare-raising	Hop
Key ring?	Atoll
Having a full set of marbles	Sane
Cellar contents?	Salt

Shenk has contributed a crossword for most of the major puzzle contests held during the past seven years. His visual and audio puzzles at the 1984 and 1985 U.S. Open tournaments caused quite a stir among contestants. In the visually clued puzzle, solvers received an extra sheet of clues containing twenty-six pictures of diverse items, each of which replaced a regular clue. Examples: photographs of Ray Bolger and Gene Wilder, answer grids from the SATs, Napoleon's signature, a drawing of a banjo, and star formations from the constellation Canis Major.

In "Here Ye, Here Ye," thirty clues were presented orally by tape. As solvers raced through the diagram filling in the blanks, they were simultaneously listening to audible clues—the theme song from *Gigi,* music by The Faces, the sound of a guitar, Barbara Mandrell's voice, and sounds made by roulette players.

Shenk's "Open Wide" playoff puzzle for the Second North Jersey Crossword Open contained references to popular TV programs, rock groups, slang, and all-round current events:

Angela Channing's grandson	Lance
1982 Barry Levinson film	Diner
Computer key	Delete
Obeys Richard Simmons	Shapes up

Shenk's metamorphosis from a constructor to an innovator came about gradually. Thus far he's done some very interesting things with crosswords. He's constructed diagramless puzzles in the shapes of a pretzel and of an hourglass. In "Sea Picture" he based a crossword around a picture placed in the center of the grid. Fifteen of the clues merely said "see picture" and each answer named one of the items in the visual. He constructed a "Scavenger Hunt" crossword for *Games* with clues related to features in that issue, e.g., "Newspaper seen on page 20" and "Ciphertext for THEY in Cryptotricks #3." Solvers had to go through the magazine to answer all the clues.

Shenk finds his inspiration for puzzles in many different sources. A quote in *Reader's Digest* caught his attention: Bob Talbert, a feature columnist for the *Detroit Free Press,* was quoted as saying, "Fame, to me, would be before I die to be 14 Down or 36 Across in a major crossword puzzle." Shenk used the exact quote in a "Wish Fulfillment" crossword and placed Talbert's first and last names in the spots he so desired. After the puzzle appeared in *Games,* Talbert wrote in his column, "Well, thanks to Mike Shenk . . . I'll die happy. . . . Shenk constructed a crossword puzzle . . . and made me 14 Down and 36 Across. . . . I'm flattered beyond crosswords."

Shenk has gone beyond traditional crosswords in his quest for ever more creative and interesting ways to look at words. When Jack Looney, vice-president and puzzle and game editor of Bantam Books, launched the Great Masters Hunt his aim was to "introduce new crossword puzzle experts to puzzle fans across the country." He felt that the search would "fill the constant need and demand for fresh challenges to crossword-puzzle addicts." The judges looked for "good diagrams, inventive themes, and fresh, contemporary clues with some flair, without being obscure." Overall, cleverness, and originality were being stressed.

Mike Shenk was one of the winners of this original contest. Since he's also one of the youngest constructors on the scene, crossword aficionados can look forward to many more years of innovative puzzling from him.

MARCHING BANDS by Mike Shenk

(SEE PAGE 266 FOR SOLUTION)

The words in this puzzle march around the grid in two ways. In one formation ("Rows"), words march across—two words for each numbered line, reading consecutively from left to right. The dividing point between these answers is for you to determine, except in row 7, where the words are separated by a black square. In the second formation ("Bands"), words march around each of the six shaded and unshaded bands, starting at the lettered squares (A, B, C, D, E, and F) and proceeding in a clockwise direction, one word after another. For example, Band "A," when filled, will contain seven consecutive words (a through g) starting in square "A" and reading around the perimeter of the grid. Band "B" will contain a series of six words (a through f) starting in square "B." Again, the dividing point between words is for you to determine. All clues are given in order. When the puzzle is completed, each square will have been used once in a Row word and once in a Band word.

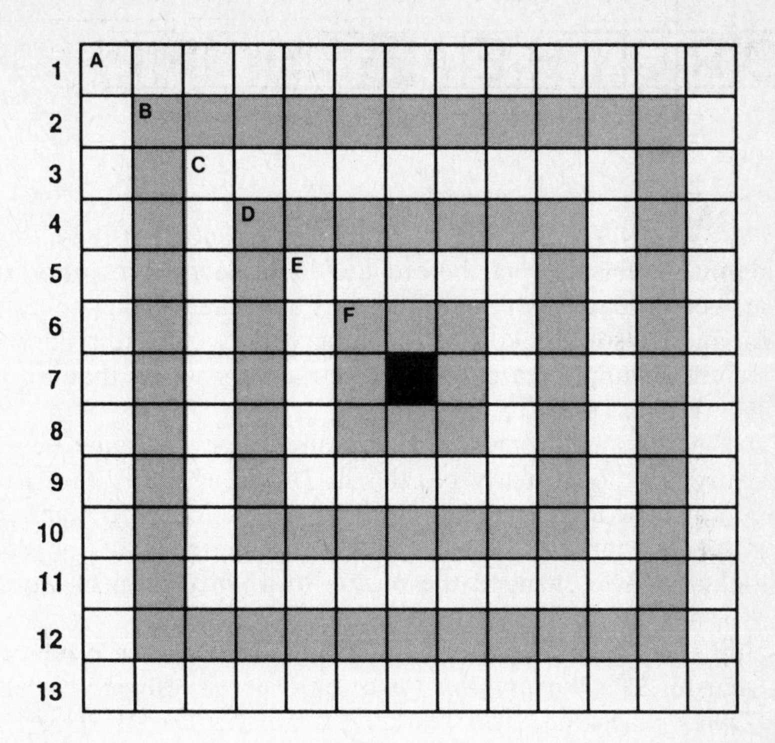

ROWS

1 a Possessive one?
b Game plan
2 a Yuletide drink
b Patriot's song
3 a Beginning
b Based on the work of a Roman philosopher
4 a Jalopy
b Theater seating section
5 a Uses a tape measure
b Shrewish ones
6 a Go by
b Muezzin's tower
7 a Water down
b Last sign of spring
8 a Compelling effect
b Ingredient of the Brewster sisters' elderberry wine
9 a Having no citizenship
b Shutterbug's concern
10 a Prop for Captain Ahab
b Straight man
11 a With the least delay
b Positive trend in profits
12 a Batman's butler
b Charles Foster Kane's last word
13 a The governor of Kansas, e.g.
b Letter strokes

BANDS

A a Hold a sit-in
b Mitch Gaylord's sport
c Football linemen
d Give the ax
e Moccasin, for one
f Fertilizer ingredient
g Circus attraction
B a Attacker
b Encouraging
c Country bumpkins
d Choose an entrée
e Parade sight
f Natural setting
C a Sleeping sickness fly
b Smooth peach
c Computer's production
d Lady of Spain
e Open square
D a Verandas
b Arthur's home
c Be inquisitive
d Brownish gray
E a Conchologist's concern
b Home of a famed monster
c Chooses
F a Move overseas

DOROTHEA SHIPP

WHEN *The National Observer* ran a none-of-the-above Presidential Plebiscite poll before the 1976 election, readers, of course, voted heavily for such favorites as Ronald Reagan, Jerry Brown, and Nelson Rockefeller. Several votes were also recorded for Dorothea Shipp, creator of some of the crosswords that ran in the *Observer* just prior to the poll.

Crosswords and politics don't usually share the same newspaper space, although early puzzles in *The New York Times* had to have a newsworthy interest, per instructions from top management. But as soon as Margaret Farrar discovered that "no one was looking," she changed the puzzle to a witty form of wordplay.

Shipp's wordplay is evident in the fifty puzzles she produces each year for *The Washington Post,* the *Christian Science Monitor, Games* magazine, *The New York Times, The Wall Street Journal,* and puzzle collections published by Simon & Schuster and Running Press. She loves to "look for themes and fit them into a puzzle." It's hard for her to figure out the exact amount of time she spends on a puzzle for she "never sits down intending to finish a puzzle then and there." She prefers to "pick them up now and again" as the mood strikes her. She has constructed a 15×15 in just over an hour, "but that was very good going." A 21×21 can take her several days or a week.

Shipp's themes cover a wide range of topics. She's used homophones and symbols as well as more traditional themes. When she used the numeral 8 for the word "ate" she received a nasty letter from a solver who wrote: "I h8 your puzzle."

She was creative with celebrities' names in "Newsmakers":

Lahr puts his auto in the garage	Bert Parks his car
Merman tends her lawn	Ethel Waters the grass
Lange is optimistic, as ever	Hope springs eternal
Gobel goofs while making breakfast	George Burns the toast
Debussy heaps invectives	Claude Rains down

She gave new meaning to familiar phrases in "Metal Detector":

Endangered bird	Auriferous eagle
Venomous snakes	Cupric heads
Tune writers' site	Stannic pan alley
Political divider	Ferric curtain
Symbol of wealth	Sterling spoon

She used symbols in a "Valentine's Special":

Zing thing, so they sing	♡string
Fireside	♡hstone
With cheer	Good ♡edly
—— Soul	♡and
Generous	Big ♡ed
February 14 honorees	Sweet ♡s
Casanova's card?	Ace of ♡s

Shipp likes to compose unusual clues. Here are her favorites:

Salesperson's nightmare	Counter attack
Monday sight	Three sheets in the wind
Campanologist's nightmare	Bluebells
Followers of Mignon and Nan	Ettes

Shipp's crossword career began in her native England when she started to solve cryptics as a teenager. She didn't start constructing, though, until the mid-sixties, by which time she was already living in the United States. (It was her husband's job with the British embassy that brought the Shipps to the States.) Her first crossword, a 23×23, was "a terrible puzzle" which has "long since gone the way of all flesh!" She "can't remember any of the clues"—after it was rejected by Margaret Farrar at the *Times* Shipp discarded it.

She did start selling her puzzles to Farrar just a short while later, after studying the rules and regulations that Farrar mailed to her with the rejection. Getting $7.50 for her first puzzle, Shipp "rushed out and bought as many copies of the newspaper" as she could when it was published. She got hooked on constructing. "I thought," she said, "that it would be a nice way to earn a little pocket money, but I just didn't realize how little it would be."

Shipp solves her daily ration of two puzzles in the comfortable setting of her farm in Greenwood, Virginia, where she lives with her husband and two horses. Although she doesn't generally clock her time, her best efforts were seven minutes for a small crossword and twenty-five minutes for a 21×21. She likes the mental stimulation she derives from solving and enjoys learning new words. She is amazed, though, "how many educated people find puzzles difficult to solve, even in university towns."

When she isn't solving or constructing puzzles, she enjoys lap swimming, riding, playing bridge, gardening, walking, and bird watching.

Dorothea Shipp, who has a degree from Reading University in England, declares that constructing crosswords educated her further: She finally learned to type!

(see next page for the puzzle)

GOLF ANYONE? by Dorothea Shipp

(*SEE PAGE 266 FOR SOLUTION*)

ACROSS

1 Strolled
7 Schoolroom adjunct
12 British sprees
18 *Esprit de corps*
19 Looked lasciviously
21 Place for a pendant
22 Johnny of football fame
23 Complete
24 Like a toadfish at times
25 Like father like son
28 Ending in chemistry
29 Squirm
30 His wife became a pillar of salt
31 Kind of crab or fish
34 Comes after sigma
37 Witch of ——
39 Kid
41 Meadowland
42 Part of a car
44 Film star Duryea or Dailey
45 Scattering of good scores?
51 Emulate the Hyades
52 Following for poet or author
53 Sun disc
54 Site for a gutter
55 Grammatical no-no
57 —— over (collapse)
58 Have empathy with
62 P.G.A. photographer's plea?
68 Golf ——
69 Mine passages
70 Compass ltrs.
71 Gov't agency
73 Relative of the weasel
75 Caboodle's companion
76 End up in the rough?
81 WW II attackers
85 Grating
86 State
87 —— *de clase*, José's schoolroom
89 Term in sewing
90 Japanese apricot
91 Edge
95 Name of a bigot's trap?
99 Pedro or Pablo
100 In —— of
101 Russian village
102 French nobility
103 Major or Minor
105 Cat or dog, for example
106 Fancy neckwear
108 Road sign
110 Exclamation of surprise
112 King of Denmark or Norway: var.
114 Groundsman's lament
121 One who loops the loop
123 —— *fideles*
124 Apprehensive
126 Basswoods
127 Bench
128 Snuggle up
129 What to do with data
130 Roman chariot
131 Smart

DOWN

1 —— Darya
2 Actress Freeman
3 —— -a-brac
4 Machine for shaping things
5 Stritch or May
6 Gloomy
7 Hebrew letter
8 Drying frame
9 Oblivion
10 Caliban's slave
11 Medical prefix
12 Necessity for most games
13 Slang ending to buck or switch
14 Expression of sorrow in bygone days
15 "Thou shalt ——"
16 Brit. award
17 But, to Caesar
20 Farmer's habitat in nursery rhymes
21 Ocean movement
26 As —— hills
27 Dumb one
32 Word in a society notice
33 Xenon or helium
34 Marble
35 Lizzie Borden's weapon
36 Little ending
38 Offs opposites
40 Kodiak or Grizzly
43 Period harmonizing lunar and solar year
45 Alcoholic beverage in Osaka
46 Feather: prefix
47 Film star Donna
48 Matriculate
49 Madison, Park or Fifth
50 Set
56 Christian symbol for Jesus
59 Bishop's title in Syria
60 Ankles
61 Tributary of the Elbe
62 —— Forest
63 Star in Draco
64 Opera singer Schipa or Gobbi
65 Offering at a material sale
66 Edgar or Candice
67 Central American tree
72 Obstinacy
73 Compass ltrs.
74 Time to be in Paris
77 Baghdad is its capital
78 Carpenter's tool
79 W. German river
80 "And the —— the morning were . . ."
82 Mountain ——

83 Skater Babilonia
84 Racing vehicle
88 People who beat up other people
90 World pwr.
92 Tuck's companion
93 Dee's predecessor
94 Shack
95 Embassy occupant: abbr.
96 —— Branco or Bravo
97 Packing oranges
98 Western coll.
103 What Mary called home across the sands of Dee
104 He rides high on the wave
107 What an elm tree provides
109 Danish money
110 Dill herbs
111 Party givers
113 Succinct
115 Nice summers
116 Recalcitrant child's word
117 —— *fixe*
118 Take notice of
119 Café advertisement
120 Film star Asther
121 "The Greatest"
122 Barsac or Medoc
125 Ottoman ruler

WILL SHORTZ

WILL SHORTZ'S NAME is familiar to the one million readers of *Games* magazine who solve the puzzles he constructs and edits for the Pencilwise section. His position as senior editor at *Games* is only one of the many positions Shortz holds in the puzzle world. He also coordinates crossword-puzzle contests, runs puzzle conventions, attends international puzzle meetings, collects rare puzzle books, corresponds with puzzlers throughout the world, and serves as puzzledom's unofficial ambassador of goodwill.

Shortz started to solve puzzles when he was a child: "When I was a kid growing up in Crawfordsville, Indiana, my mother limited us to one hour of television a day. Other kids watched television. I did puzzles—book after book of them."

He created his first crossword when he was only nine. As he remembers, "My mother was trying to keep me quiet for an afternoon while her bridge club was over, so she gave me a large sheet of paper, ruled it into squares, and started me on a crossword. Later she showed me how to number the grid and write the clues."

Shortz started submitting puzzles for publication and sold his first one to *Venture,* a Presbyterian youth magazine, when he was fourteen. Two years later, he devised a "Time Test" puzzle column for Dell Publishing Company and asked his speech teacher to recommend him without revealing his age. (At that time, Dell required recommendations for new contributors.) He was afraid that Dell would either take advantage of him or refuse to run the column if they knew that he was only sixteen. Fortunately, they did neither, and the feature ran for several years.

Shortz earned the only known bachelor's degree in puzzle making, or "enigmatology." After completing all the course requirements to satisfy his major in economics, he embarked on Indiana University's Independent Learning Program with self-constructed tutorials such as "The Development of Word Puzzles in Great Britain from 1700 to 1850," "The Psychology of Puzzle Solvers," and "A Study of Anagrams."

His senior thesis, "The History of American Word Puzzles to

1860," traced the development of puzzles from a literary manifestation of the most learned writers to a popular pastime in mass-market magazines. His meticulous research unearthed the first word puzzles published in America, twelve riddles from Samuel Danforth's 1647 almanac. This verse for the month of April is typical of them:

> That which hath neither tongue nor wings
> This month how merrily it sings
> To see such, out for dead who lay
> To cast their winding sheets away?
> Friends! would you live? some pils then take
> When head and stomack both doe ake.

Scholars believe that "that which hath neither tongue nor wings" refers to a brook—the verse is addressed to those who shed their winter illnesses and grew healthier in the spring.

Part of Shortz's present-day fame derives from his being a crossword tournament director. He entered the tournament scene in 1978 when the sales manager of the Stamford, Connecticut, Marriott Hotel decided to hold a crossword competition on what would otherwise have been an underbooked winter weekend. With Eugene T. Maleska's help he found the ideal contest coordinator right in his own backyard: Shortz was living and working in Stamford and had recently co-founded the Fairfield County Puzzlers (FCP) club.

Early in his career Shortz began to use his organizational skills to bring puzzlers together for a variety of formal and informal occasions. His first challenge was the National Puzzlers' League (NPL).

Formed in 1883, the NPL's aim was threefold: "to provide a pastime of mental relaxation for lovers of word puzzles, to raise the standard of puzzling to a higher intellectual level and to establish and foster friendships among its widely scattered members." The league's monthly magazine, *The Enigma,* is filled with anagrams, charades, enigmas, beheadments, transpositions, and other wordplay popular in the late nineteenth century, when pre-crossword puzzling reached its pinnacle.

Conventions were an integral part of the NPL from its inception until 1958, when inertia and a waning membership threatened the league's existence. Recognizing that the league's survival depended on increased enthusiasm from current members and an infusion of new blood (preferably young), Shortz persuaded another league member, Helene Hovanec, to join forces with him to reinstitute the conventions after an eighteen-year hiatus. The first "modern" convention in Princeton, New Jersey, in August 1976 attracted only twenty-seven members, but it was so successful that it spawned a succession of increasingly big annual get-togethers.

Shortz, aided by league members, has served as program chairman for each convention. His marathon solving sessions include small and large team games as well as individual competitions.

During a library trivia hunt at the centennial convention, four-person teams delved into the reference books at the Rutgers University Library to find the answers to forty incredibly trivial questions like these (answers are on page 208):

1. According to *Pugh's Dictionary of Acronyms and Abbreviations,* what's an OBOE?
2. When the Emmy Awards were presented for best shows of March 1973–March 1974, what program won for "Outstanding Game Show, Daytime Programming"?
3. In what city was Art Garfunkel born?
4. On what day did Easter fall in 1776?

"Definitions," based on the TV game show *Wheel of Fortune,* has been played enthusiastically at several conventions. Contestants guess the answers to outrageous puns through a combination of definitions and letter placement in words. The host says the punny definition and then writes out the numeration of the words in the answer by placing a series of blanks on the chalkboard. Members call out letters, one a time, and the host places them in the appropriate blanks. Examples of the puns include:

A worthless auction purchase	Gyp off the old block
Gutted building	Edifice wrecks
Eric the Red	A Norse of a different color
X-rated orchestra instruments	Sax and violins

In "Characteristic Initials," the names of famous people were described by phrases using their initials:

Wacky Artist	Woody Allen
Partner To Bailey	P. T. Barnum
Displays Pulchritude	Dolly Parton

In the individual contests members solve puzzles similar to those in *The Enigma* or more lighthearted fare such as those from Shortz's *Brain Games* books (answers are on page 209):

"Remove one letter from each word below, and rearrange those that remain to spell a common metal":

LODGE
GROIN
ADDLE
CROPPED
REVISAL

It was after his success with the NPL that Shortz turned his energies toward forming the Fairfield County Puzzlers (FCP). Through his editorial job at Penny Press, producers of mass-market puzzle magazines, Shortz contacted Stephanie Spadaccini, a constructor whose work he admired. She shared his enthusiasm, and together they persuaded five additional Fairfield County crossword constructors to join them. The first meeting, in 1977, generated enough enthusiasm to start monthly meetings. The group, still in existence, focuses on crossword puzzles, with a particular emphasis on construction. Members discuss and solve puzzles, play word games and chat.

Thus Shortz could readily accept the challenge of designing and running a crossword contest, knowing that the club members were willing to act as judges. He commissioned top constructors Maura Jacobson, Jordan Lasher, Jack Luzzatto, and Tap Osborn to create new puzzles; devised a scoring and checking system; and planned an evening of lively word games to complement the rigorous solving schedule. When Margaret Farrar offered to "assist in any way possible," he asked her to award the prizes, which she did until her death in 1984.

The first year 161 crossword addicts traveled across and down Connecticut to spend a weekend solving crosswords, playing games, chatting with people of like interests and meeting constructors. Mostly middle-class and middle-aged, they paved the way for what

Judges David and Anne Griswold with the clock used to time contestants during the solving rounds

has become the most popular crossword weekend in the United States.

Contestants, separated by dividers, squared off against each other and tackled four puzzles of varying sizes (15 × 15 to 21 × 21) and time limits (fifteen to forty-five minutes). The tension and silence were reminiscent of College Board examinations except during Maura Jacobson's "Movies You May Have Missed" crossword as solvers chuckled appreciatively upon discovering these clues:

French Tarzan's adventures	*Degaulle of the Wild*
Changing times in the nursery	*The Didy Dozen*
Sex on the reservation	*Lust of the Mohicans*
Top bookie	*The Wizard of Odds*

Unfortunately, Shortz hadn't foreseen the pitfalls inherent in setting up a scoring system based on the correct number of letters, rather than words. Solvers rapidly figured out that the placement of an "E" in any blank space would increase their chances of a higher score. Judges rapidly discovered that the "E" ploy greatly increased the amount of time needed to score the puzzles.

Shortz had also underestimated the amount of help he needed. Since the actual judging didn't begin until after the evening entertainment, the five judges spent a sleepless night going over all 644 papers (161 contestants times four rounds). Literally racing against the clock, they completed the judging and posted the preliminary results seconds before the fifth and final round began on Sunday morning.

In subsequent years Shortz rectified these mistakes by recruiting a dozen judges, marking each puzzle upon completion of the round, setting up a scoring system based on correct words, and with Mike Shenk's expertise, using a computer to tally the scores and print out the standings.

Shortz joined *Games* in 1979 in a manner unbefitting a puzzle editor, but serendipitous nevertheless. He misread the clues for a blind Position Wanted ad. Believing that the "quality puzzle publication" seeking an editor with "new ideas" was *Games,* Shortz walked unannounced into editor Mike Donner's office and applied for the job. Although Donner hadn't placed the ad, he was sufficiently impressed with Shortz's credentials to offer him a freelance position on the spot. In just a short while Shortz moved to a full-time position and worked his way up to senior editor. Shortz never did discover who placed that ad.

Shortz's Pencilwise section in *Games* is filled with witty, sophisticated word and picture play in the form of crosswords, cryptics, cryptograms, word searches, Double-Crostics, mazes, and a seemingly never-ending range of variety puzzles, many of them Shortz's original creations (and sometimes camouflaged under the pseudonyms of A. Braine and Sarah Bellum).

In "The World's Most Ornery Crossword," a *Games* staple, solvers have a choice of "hard" or "easy" clues with the differences between the two being rather substantial:

Easy	**Hard**	**Answer**
Powerlessness	Power outage?	Impotence
Sally and Ayn	Q-T connectors?	Rands
Worms, minnows, etc.	This can get hooked	Bait
Church levy equal to 10%	Decimate, in a way	Tithe
Very thin, as a fracture	Victim of a recession?	Hairline
Soft drink	Tab, for one	Soda
Egyptian mothers?	They're kept under wraps	Mummies

The "ornery" crossword was invented by Donner. Shortz has continued to include it in each issue because it's so popular with *Games* solvers.

Flyer for the first of the modern crossword tournaments. The 1978 contest was so popular that it has become an annual event, held each spring at the Stamford Marriott Hotel in Stamford, Connecticut.

David Griswold double-checks a contestant's entry.

Another popular *Games* features is "Wacky Wordies," in which the unique placement of letters and/or symbols represents familiar expressions. Shortz and his staff created the puzzles for the original "Wacky Wordies" feature and through the years thousands of readers have sent in their own clever examples (answers are on page 209):

.that's	H-O-P-E-S
SOMething	head ache
3. O 2. U 1. T	wire just
ieieceiie	momanon

Shortz seems to have a limitless supply of ideas for clever puzzles, but if he ever needs inspiration he can refer to any of the four thousand puzzle books in his collection, methodically arranged by categories—Crossword Puzzles, Classical Word Puzzles, Codes and Ciphers, Mechanical and Manipulative Puzzles, Mystery and Detective Puzzles. Many of his books are priceless antiques he found by scouring used bookstores in every city he visits. He also has a network of dealers who tell him about any puzzle books they acquire.

Shortz maintains a voluminous correspondence with puzzle constructors, historians, and experts all over the world. His office at *Games* serves as an unofficial clearinghouse about puzzle activities everywhere. Through his unofficial status as puzzledom's ambassador he has traveled to Eastern bloc puzzle conventions in Hungary and Czechoslovakia and crossword tournaments in England. He's probably the only person in the world who solves puzzles in Italian, French, Hungarian, Serbo-Croatian, and numerous other languages he doesn't speak.

He's also the most well-known Western puzzle maker in Eastern European countries. He was interviewed in Rumania for a

Radio Free Europe broadcast and was written up in newspapers in Poland, Hungary, and Yugloslavia. He even wrote a crossword article, "Call My Bluff," for a Yugoslavian puzzle magazine. The article contained ten items about crosswords. Readers had to determine if they were true or false, e.g., "At one time the *San Francisco Chronicle* printed advertising in the black squares of its crossword" (True) and "Boy George's father was one of the crossword puzzle editors for the London *Daily Telegraph*" (False).

Shortz is an advocate of new-wave clues, those that rely more on wordplay than factual knowledge, with a stress on current words, slang, names, and music. New-wave constructors avoid obscure words, classical literature, opera, and arcane facts. Here are some examples from *Games* of novel ways to clue familiar words. These clues were written by Shortz, his staff, and the constructors whose work appears in *Games*:

Quickly, quickly	ASAP
Hole-some food?	Donut
Reading material?	Palm
Parachutist's opening?	Geronimo
Holy city of Ohio?	Toledo
Having more smarts?	Sorer
Joint material	Pot

In a field in which specialists predominate, Shortz is a Renaissance man interested in all types of puzzles and all facets of the puzzle world. He has accomplished so much already in his thirty-four years, demonstrating his expertise in numerous ways—as author of the popular *Brain Game* books, puzzles based on clever wordplay, and *World Class Championship Crosswords,* the definitive book on crossword contests; creator of hundreds of different types of puzzles; author of puzzle articles for a variety of publications; and mentor to new constructors.

ANSWERS—SHORTZ

Library Trivia Hunt

1. Offshore Buoy Observing Equipment
2. *Password* (found in *TV Facts,* 1980)
3. Forest Hills, N.Y. (found in *Who's Who in America*)
4. March 30 (found in Bond's *Handy-Book for Verifying Dates, etc.*)

Brain Games

1. Gold
2. Iron
3. Lead
4. Copper
5. Silver

Wacky Wordies

1. That's beside the point
2. Dashed hopes
3. Start of something big
4. Splitting headache
5. Outnumbered three to one
6. Just under the wire
7. "I before E except after C"
8. Man in the moon

SQUARE ROUTES by Will Shortz

(SEE PAGE 266 FOR SOLUTION)

Square Routes is a word game within a puzzle. Each clue consists of three words that can precede or follow a fourth word to complete a compound word or a familiar two-word phrase. For example, the clue words LIST, BOOT, and HOLE would lead to the answer BLACK (to complete BLACKLIST, BOOTBLACK, and BLACK HOLE). To solve, first answer as many clues as you can. Then enter each answer in the grid, beginning in the square corresponding to the clue number and proceeding in any horizontal, vertical, or diagonal direction. (The direction can be determined by logic and the crossing letters of other answers.) Work back and forth between grid and clues to finish. When you're done, every square in the grid will be filled, and at least half the letters of each word will be crossed by other answers.

CLUES

1	Cooker	Blood	Atmospheric
2	Beauty	Walking	Wear
3	Paint	Elbow	Pencil
4	Yule	Rolling	Cabin
5	Suit	Martial	Abiding
6	Acid	Check	Dance
7	Agent	Space	Sickness
8	Knife	Club	Rib
9	Mud	Arm	Match
10	Horse	Track	Belly
11	Lock	Memo	Knee
12	Stock	Taking	Paper
13	Word	Mountain	Key

1		2				3		4
		5				6	7	
				8				
9					10			
		11						12
			13	14		15		16
			17				18	19
20	21			22	23			
24			25		26		27	

14	Winner	Basket	Ginger
15	Snake	Death	Brained
16	Busy	Traffic	Corps
17	Around	Catch	Fours
18	Butter	Gallery	Roasted
19	Deep	Level	Port
20	Deck	Latin	Finals
21	Brown	Daddy	Cane
22	Tennis	Tree	Gum
23	Scotch	Bunny	Bell
24	Car	Vice	Firing
25	Speed	Door	Mouse
26	Corn	Art	Soda
27	Working	Letter	Punishment

LOIS SIDWAY

DOWN TO EARTH Lois Sidway spends a lot of time up in the air. As the wife of a TWA pilot she takes advantage of the discount fares available to her and often visits relatives.

In fact, it was a visit to her brother-in-law that sparked her interest in crossword constructing. A would-be constructor, he had just received a rejection letter from Eugene T. Maleska for a Sunday-size puzzle he had created. Maleska advised the novice to tackle a 15×15 crossword—"Instead of starting with a symphony, why not start with an étude?" Maleska's rejection packet included a copy of the *Times*'s style sheet. Sidway and her brother-in-law "were enchanted to read the rejection letter," because they had never thought about the human element behind each puzzle.

Her brother-in-law's experience inspired Sidway to try her own hand at constructing. On the flight home she took out an unused *Times* crossword and filled in the blanks with words related to dogs:

Live like Lassie	Lead a dog's life
Dognappers et al.	Villains
Kind of spaniel	Water
Firedogs	Irons
Part for Boomer	Role
——and Englishmen	Mad dogs
Malamute's medic	Vet
Eskimo's best friend?	Husky

Sidway packed more than twenty thematic entries into the diagram and mailed it to Maleska. His acceptance letter congratulated her on an amazing feat—having her very first construction accepted by the *Times*. Maleska wrote, "You are a *rara avis,* for very few people have had their first puzzles accepted."

Sidway had joined the elite ranks of those who construct crosswords, but she had to wait a year to see her puzzle in print. Maleska has such a wealth of material in his stockpile that the average interval between acceptance and publication is about twelve months.

Sidway's husband was in Saudi Arabia on the day her first puzzle appeared in print, but was able to solve it because the *Times*'s crosswords are also published in *The International Herald-Tribune*.

Sidway continued to send puzzles to Maleska, some of which were accepted. Among the rejections was a rebus-type puzzle in which the word "love" was replaced with a symbol of a heart. Maleska suggested that Sidway might find a market for this puzzle in *Games* magazine and directed her to Will Shortz. Shortz couldn't use the puzzle either, but he invited Sidway to join the Fairfield County Puzzlers after noting her New Canaan, Connecticut, address. She accepted and became one its most active members. Later she joined the puzzle contest scene by becoming a judge at the Marriott tourney.

Sidway is an extremely organized person and her contribution to the smooth running of the Marriott tournament is much appreciated by Shortz and the other judges. A slim, attractive woman with touches of gray in her short, curly hair, Sidway is soft-spoken, gentle, and efficient. Largely because of Sidway and Anne and Dave Griswold the judging procedure runs like clockwork from the moment that the first paper is collected to the awarding of the final prizes.

Sidway's construction career continued to develop during the early 1980s. Editors heard about her abilities through the puzzle grapevine and in just a short while she found her puzzles appearing regularly in the daily *New York Times, Games, Dell Champion Crossword Puzzles, TV Crosswords,* and magazines published by Official Publications and Penny Press.

Sidway's rapid growth as a constructor is even more remarkable because she didn't start solving crosswords until adulthood. She pieced together jigsaws by the dozens during her childhood in Enid, Oklahoma (a name frequently found in crossword puzzles), but didn't attempt to solve crosswords until the early sixties. At that time, she and her husband spent much of their Sundays solving the *Times* puzzle. Sidway started her solo solving only after her three young sons were in school full time.

Sidway never let puzzles interfere with her domestic responsibilities, but now that her sons are grown and have families of their own, she's free to devote as much time as she likes to constructing the seventy-five to one hundred puzzles she sells each year. Her specialty is 15 × 15 thematic crosswords with themes covering a wide range of topics.

A "British Style" crossword used the English spellings of familiar words:

Focal point for Queen Victoria	Centre of gravity
Medium for a Churchill message	Radio programme
Tactics for Tommy Atkins	Army manoeuvres
Professional lorry drivers, et al.	Organised labour

In "Minor Alterations" Sidway changed one letter in familiar expressions and clued each one cleverly:

Requirement for Cinderella?	The shoe must go on
Pickled rustic?	Farmer in the dill
Mug for the camera?	Put on a sappy face

In "Boo" she used a Halloween theme:

Group of trick-or-treaters?	Skeleton crew
Low-down hijinks on Halloween?	Skullduggery
Have an intuition, like a ghoul?	Feel in one's bones
What Halloween taffy apples do?	Stick to one's ribs

One of Sidway's favorite puzzles was tersely titled "!" and included the following phrases, all defined as mild expletives—I'll be hornswoggled!" "Well, well!" "Sufferin' succotash!"

In "Parking Spaces" solvers had to fill in the blanks with a picture of a "car" to complete these words: Miss Lillian CARter, called on the CARpet, CARpenter ants, and reinCARnation.

In her "Where's the Beef?" puzzle the thematic entries—"Oxymoron," "steerage," "cowardly," and "bulletins"—were clued without any indication of their association with animals. Along the same lines, her "Urbane Men" crossword gradually revealed the hidden theme, city surnames, with these clues:

Eyre's man	Edward Rochester
Adelaide's man	Nathan Detroit
42nd Street man	Busby Berkeley
"Bop Till You Drop" man	Rick Springfield

Sidway used a variation of an old form of wordplay, curtailments, for a puzzle in which the definitions descended in order through the diagram:

Out of the running	Finished
Come to a close	Finish
Final curtain	Finis
Over and done with	Fini

Sidway likes puzzles that are fun for both constructor and solver. One of her favorites is "Anyone for Tennis?" which included:

Ace?	Point of no return
McEnroe misdemeanor?	Contempt of court
Some disputed calls?	Borderline cases

Although she doesn't consider herself a new-wave constructor (she loves opera and peppers her puzzles with arias and singers), she's not averse to using punny clues like these:

Worms to an early bird	Diet
Cézanne's summers	Etés
Psacred psong	Psalm
Ex–German movie star	Rin Tin Tin

Sidway constructs puzzles at home, "sitting on the living-room sofa" and uses the various word finders, dictionaries, encyclopedias, and crossword dictionaries that are the stock-in-trade of most constructors. Since she does travel so much, she often takes her work with her. On a six-hour flight to Europe, piloted by her husband, Sidway spent the entire time poring over a diagram, constructing a puzzle. It was a time-consuming chore for she had no reference books with her. A fellow passenger, believing that she was solving a difficult crossword, stopped by her seat to commiserate, "Boy, that must be a *real* toughie!"

PERSONALS by Lois Sidway

(SEE PAGE 267 FOR SOLUTION)

ACROSS

1 A few
5 Umpire's home away from home?
10 Muffled bark
14 It could be heavy
15 Tended the Tin Man
16 One of a musical group
19 Actor's natty accessory?
21 Describing some minds
23 Vera's plant?
24 Scrooge, for one
25 City on the Loire
27 Diminutive suffix
28 Dawson of football
29 Connection
30 Response to "Shall we?"
31 Grow weak
32 Malaga mom
34 Lucy's hubby
36 Commercial award
37 Endures
38 Some beach boys
40 Command
42 Restrain
43 "The —— Texas . . ."
45 Cheese counter items
46 Be in accord
48 Strikes out, editorially
50 —— sec (pronto)
51 Head-of-statesman
53 "—— tricks?"
56 Marine excavator
58 —— *Time Next Year*
59 Cry of surprise
60 Infamous Amin
61 Detective's unusual pet?
63 Scholarly lexicon: abbr.
64 Soft material
66 The Von Trapps had quite a few
67 Swelling mass, as of smoke
69 No ifs, —— or buts
70 Deceptive
72 *Bar-le-* —— (currant preserve)
73 Shackles
75 Repetitive recital
76 Grades
78 Figures of speech
81 —— time (never)
82 Fish-eating seabird
83 Des ——, Iowa
85 Uncle in children's fiction
87 Relative of a rabbit
88 Trial
91 English muffin's relative
92 Formerly, once
93 Klutz
94 Wax eloquent
96 Becoming slower, in mus.
97 Thus, to Cato
98 Funny lady Hawn
100 Pickle juice
101 Mine, to Marceau
102 Kind of chitchat
104 Singer's party favor?
107 Sweet German bread
108 Silly
109 Great amounts of money: slang
110 Equal
111 Stingingly sapid
112 "Simon ——"

DOWN

1 Following the first point
2 Will- —— -wisp
3 Meadow cry
4 Varnish resin
5 Job, down under
6 Authorized street vendor, for one
7 Winged
8 Bo's number
9 Paradise
10 "I —— Be Happy": Caesar/Youmans, 1924
11 S-curved arches
12 Chooses
13 Evergreen
14 Odometer reading
16 Butcher's phrase, re roasts
17 Fabulous feller's foot woe?
18 Striking effect
19 Swedish seaport
20 Told a fib
22 Saint Bernards' burdens
26 "—— well that ends well." (Heywood)
29 Pithy
31 Long way
33 Orchestra section
35 Violet-blue
36 Deep sleep
37 "Clair de ——"
39 Auctioneer's word
41 Ex-mayor's cooking mishap?
42 Small bay
44 Potted display of maidenhairs
46 Reassure
47 Caught with a lasso
49 Run-down
51 Soprano Amelita —— -Curci
52 Warren Beatty film
53 Stereo's predecessor
54 *Island of the Blue Dolphins* author

55 Actor's lap occupant
57 MDs
58 Impresario Hurok
62 Croquet hoop
65 Tsk tsk
66 Entertainer Sonny
68 Bounder
69 Jellied salad
71 Without
72 Copenhagen native
74 Lariat loop
76 Tuesday, in New Orleans
77 Word with wheel or committee
79 Gigantic
80 Prom guests
82 Tend the posies
84 Begin, as darkness
85 Remainder
86 New York Indians
87 *Catch-22* author
89 Mole role for Guinness
90 Mr. Randall
93 Generous
95 Camp structures
98 Strong wind
99 Send out
100 Fiber source
101 Hail from a sailor
103 Better
105 Miscellany
106 —— Na Na

RICHARD SILVESTRI

RICHARD SILVESTRI, an assistant professor of mathematics at Nassau Community College in Garden City, New York, constructs puzzles around entertaining themes. Since he says he has "always considered it a matter of honor to tackle a crossword puzzle unaided by reference books," he feels that puzzle solvers shouldn't have to use outside sources either. He tries to avoid "such abominations as 'Hungarian mezzo-soprano' and 'duodenal ulcer: French' " in his clues. Silvestri doesn't even own an unabridged dictionary because he feels that having too many reference works around would tempt him to use obscure words. After completing his diagram he goes to the library to do any necessary fact-checking.

Solvers don't have to linger too long over Silvestri's puzzles—most can be solved without too much difficulty, once you catch his style. From "For Birdbrains":

17th-century avian epic?	Parrotise lost
Popular saying re lovebirds	Toucan live as cheap as swan
Hatchling?	Next dove kin
Prehistoric bird?	Crow magnon
Modern aviary?	Condorminium
Rebirth of ornithology?	Wrenaissance

From "Refuse Collection":

Antiquary's refusal?	Never in a million years
Boxer's refusal?	Count me out
Idler's refusal?	Nothing doing
Astronomer's refusal?	Far be it from me
Euphemist's refusal?	Like heck I will
Judge's refusal	Try and make me
Arbitrator's refusal?	Under no circumstances
Biographer's refusal	Not on your life
Despot's refusal?	Absolutely not

From "Capitalism":

Fruit of the vine	Concord grapes
Tennis star	Tracy Austin
1770 event	Boston Massacre
JFK's press secretary	Pierre Salinger
October 12, formerly	Columbus Day

From "Redundancies":

Dark red rope	Maroon strand
Undresses combos	Strips bands
Heading for April	Spring bound
Indecent reprimand	Rank rating
Barn-building company	Stable firm

From "Heteronyms" (words that are spelled alike but differ in sound and sense):

First writing implement?	Lead pencil
Very small dance?	Minute waltz
Nile denizen sprees?	Crocodile tears
Hall of wax?	Polish corridor

From "Foreign Correspondence":

Morte	Death in Venice
Fenêtres	French windows
Schafer	German shepherd
La lluvia	The rain in Spain

Silvestri's nonthematic clues are just as clever:

When Nancy gets hot	Eté
A fate worse than debt	Default
Turn of the page	Errand
It's not every player's forte	Piano
Crow's feat	Caw
They're not at home	Basemen
The reel thing?	Tape

Silvestri started to solve puzzles when he was only five years old. He liked the rebuses and riddles in *Jack and Jill* and *Humpty Dumpty*. However, he didn't start to solve crosswords until he was an undergraduate at Colgate University.

The New York Times was delivered to his dorm every Sunday and one copy of the newspaper was put in the lounge. The early risers would spirit away the most popular sections, e.g., sports. By the time Silvestri and his friends reached the lounge in late morning, one of the few sections left would be the magazine. Silvestri's group would gather round the puzzle and try to solve it en masse. As they got more proficient, they got much more competitive about their solving. Somehow or other they'd rustle up other copies of the puzzle and compete against each other to see who could solve the fastest. By the time Silvestri graduated he was almost always the first to finish.

In graduate school at Adelphi, Silvestri began solving the cryptics in *New York* magazine and eventually began to create his own. Surprisingly, Silvestri had never constructed a traditional crossword.

When he did construct his first 15 × 15 crossword in 1977 he mailed it to Eugene Maleska at the *Times*. It was rejected because Maleska felt that "fifty black squares" were "a bit too much for a fifteen by fifteen puzzle" (the average is about thirty-six).

Silvestri tried again and this time his puzzle was accepted. Maleska's note was both congratulatory—"I like your puzzle very much"—and querying—"I need your sources for the trio of Groucho entries" (the theme of the puzzle was Groucho Marx characters).

Maleska played a major role in boosting Silvestri's crossword career. Says Silvestri of his mentor: "He included constructive criticism in his letters of acceptance; referred my work to Dell Publishing Company; suggested that *Attenzione* magazine include me in a piece about top constructors (*Attenzione* covered the crossword scene in its September 1981 issue); and gave me a very nice write-up in his book *Across and Down.*"

Silvestri followed Maleska's advice: "When a puzzle is finished, go over it with a fine comb. Make alterations like Keats." He feels that his work has improved considerably under Maleska's tutelage: "I now take greater care in limiting the number of black squares in puzzles and in banishing 'crosswordese.' I think (hope) that I've never constructed a puzzle in which two obscure entries cross."

Another result of Maleska's influence is that the publicity Silvestri received from being in his book resulted in an increased number of offers to construct puzzles for various editors. In addition to the *Times* and Dell Publications, Silvestri's work appears in the Simon & Schuster books, the Running Press series, Will Weng's *Crossword Club,* the *Times* books and *Math and Computer Education Journal.*

Silvestri's careers as a crossword constructor and college educator usually don't overlap. However, Silvestri's expertise in crosswords was indirectly responsible for landing him his first full-time teaching job. He had sent a résumé to the chairman of the math department at a small college. Coincidentally, Silvestri's crossword, with by-line, appeared in the Sunday *Times* on the same day that the math chairman was leafing through résumés. Putting two and two together, he interviewed Silvestri over the telephone and hired him.

When Silvestri was interviewed for his present position the committee spent a lot of time questioning him about his crossword activities. They had already decided to hire him, but were very interested in discussing crosswords.

Silvestri is a bachelor in his late thirties. He's a wonderful conversationalist, peppering his comments with witty wordplay. In his spare time he likes to listen to fifties rock 'n' roll music and root for the New York Yankees.

Not many of Silvestri's students solve crosswords. However, during the week that one of Silvestri's puzzles is scheduled to appear in the Sunday *Times* he will offer extra credit to students who solve that puzzle. No one has ever handed him a complete solution, but he's gotten lots of partially completed puzzles from his students.

For creating crosswords that satisfy solvers' needs for a quick, amusing bout of mental gymnastics, Silvestri, the college teacher, is himself awarded high marks.

LETTER SHIFTS by Richard Silvestri

(SEE PAGE 267 FOR SOLUTION)

ACROSS

1 Upright
6 Barely finish in the money
10 —— *for Adano*
15 Earn a D
19 Psalm word
20 Author Morrison
21 Millrose Games event
22 "—— boy!"
23 A picture puzzle about the son of Chaos
26 Spare
27 Mazel ——
28 One of *Them!*
29 Hung loosely
30 Chin warmer
31 Dodger's activity
34 Eve's opposite
35 Serenade the villain
36 Appraises
37 Viz.: drag the thing away
41 Three before vee
44 "—— hurts when I laugh"
46 Former Supreme
47 Puff up
48 Reverence
49 Wax: prefix
50 Sorrowful exclamation
52 Freudian subject
53 Caddy contents
54 The man competes against the woman's best runners
59 Partake of victuals
60 Peeved
62 Beatles' "—— Work It Out"
63 Babble
65 He played Barney Fife
66 Navigation system
67 Rented
68 Prefix for path
69 Zenana
70 Gate or golfer
72 From —— Z
73 Dad loans scraps to a friend
77 Batter after Babe
78 Iceman's tool
79 Take part in a children's game
80 Eur./Afr. divider
83 Gallery display
84 Coeur d'——, Idaho
85 Armstrong's was historic
87 Infer
90 D.C. VIP
91 Bleak, the way a Nile deity used to be
93 Haarlem bloom
94 Redding of song
96 In the thick of
97 Platitude
99 Doled
101 Ancient Roman brigade
104 Pub pint
105 Marciano's favorite number?
106 Bouquet
107 Frenzied antelope got ashore
111 Responsibility
112 Express a view
113 Flying bowman
114 Deal in hot stuff
115 Prom partner
116 Chose
117 Durham campus
118 Carried

DOWN

1 Arcane
2 Make as good as new
3 Skyscraper necessity
4 DeSoto or LaSalle
5 Bronx leader
6 Smarted
7 Party giver
8 Lennon's lady
9 Sites for some dressers
10 Infamous
11 Gridlock sound
12 Hamburg's river
13 Sing the praises of
14 1918 battle site
15 Goes white
16 A flirt relaxing
17 Night light
18 George who was a woman
24 Interdiction
25 "To —— is human . . ."
30 Quick meal
32 Room for relaxation
33 Christmas or Easter: abbr.
34 Bullwinkle, e.g.
35 Request at the blackjack table
37 Religious leaflet
38 Earthling
39 City on the Allegheny
40 Brit. servicewoman
42 Place for a letter
43 In a chair
45 Tall tales
51 Chou En- ——
52 Run away
54 Execrate
55 Bar at the bar
56 They serve a duel purpose
57 Toast starter

58 Shell out
60 Set aside for the future
61 All tipsters away
64 Joplin output
65 Eucalyptus eaters
66 Hope and Jessica
67 Did an inside job?
69 Auburn dye
70 Loses traction
71 Tie the knot
74 Hold-up man of myth
75 Theater chain magnate
76 In front
80 Belligerent
81 Proof
82 Was contingent
84 Unirrigated
85 Where Pago Pago is
86 Paired
88 Ike's W.W. II command
89 Jamaican export
92 Did some fencing
95 To the point
97 Jaded
98 It's seen in anger
99 Subjunctive, for one
100 Best of the theater
101 Nomadic Norseman
102 Wield a blue pencil
103 Heredity factor
104 A way to run
107 Bossy sound
108 Actress Joanne
109 Triton
110 Sign of summer

MEL TAUB

Mel Taub often solves crosswords on the subway, going from his office in Manhattan to his home in Brooklyn. One evening his rapid solving attracted the attention of a fellow straphanger, who complimented him on this remarkable feat. He graciously acknowledged her praise without revealing that he was "in the business." They continued to meet sporadically and she was always impressed with his speedy solving. One evening she asked Taub to demonstrate his skill to a friend who was with her. Taub happened to have the Sunday *Times* magazine with him, so he turned to a puns and anagrams puzzle. To the astonishment of the woman and her friend, Taub whizzed through the diagram in only a couple of minutes. After reveling in their applause, he confessed to being the constructor of the puzzle. They didn't believe him until he showed them some identification.

To puns and anagrams solvers, Taub needs no identification. He claims to have inherited this specialty by default because some of the regular puns and anagrams constructors stopped working on them. Also, Margaret Farrar liked to use his puzzles because "she didn't have to break her neck editing them."

For the uninitiated, the clues to puns and anagrams are based on wordplay. Solvers look for whole and partial anagrams, puns, homophones, deletions, charades, and abbreviations. Many of the clues are similar to those used in cryptic crosswords, but without the stringent rules. While purists might object to the lack of dual cluing (a straight definition and a wordplay definition), most aficionados revel in the often outrageous humor of the genre.

Here are some examples of the kinds of wordplay Taub uses in puns and anagrams puzzles:

Anagrams—rearranging the letters in one word to form a new word:

> "Setting for a cello" = "locale," anagram of "a cello"
> "Ran O.K. at tire center" = "Akron," anagram of "ran O.K."

Anagram/Deletions—removing the letters from a longer word and rearranging the remaining letters to form a new word:

"Did Parisian rogue go off here?" = "rue," "go" removed from "rogue"

"Get that from attachés" = "Case," "that" removed from "attaches"

"She finds Martin artless" = "Min," "art removed from Martin"

Puns—plays on words:

"Kind of ache?" = "mist," pun on "mistake"

"Start of a long game" = "tag," pun on "tag along"

Homophones—using words to represent letters of the alphabet:

"Did Ellen cue Sam or Tom?" = "Uncle," anagram of "cue" and "L+N" (Ellen)

"Blockhead one might see nude" = "dunce," anagram of "nude" and "C" (see)

Roman numerals—changing Arabic numbers to Roman numerals to represent the letters C, D, I, L, M, V, and X:

"Safe place for a hen around 5 a.m." = "haven," anagram of "a hen" and "V" (5)

"52 ct. purchase is lawful" = "licit," anagram of "LII" (52) and "ct"

Numbers—using numbers to indicate which letters of a longer word make up the answer word:

"Bedroom 3,547 students use" = "dorm," the third, fifth, fourth, and seventh letters of "bedroom"

"They supervise 4,137 Germans" = "mgrs.," the fourth, first, third, and seventh letters of "Germans"

Charades/partial charades—breaking a word down into its components and providing definitions for each part:

"De wine in de decanter" = "deport"

"Where de antelope play" = "derange"

"Bird that begins late?" = "emu," for "emulate"

"It came before you ate" = "sit," for "situate"

Hidden answers—burying the answer word in the clue:

"Spanish heart" = "ani," middle of "Spanish"

"He was serving in middle of hearing" = "Ervin," buried in "serving"

Taub is so identified with puns and anagrams that it's hard to think of his constructing any other type of puzzle. But he's one of the few constructors who has mastered many different types of puzzles.

His puzzle experiences began when he was in the fifth grade. From rebus-style puzzles, he graduated to crosswords as a teenager and rapidly reached a point where he could solve a 13 × 13 in five or ten minutes. He spent a lot of his free time in college solving the *New York Times* crossword puzzle.

Taub toyed with constructing a crossword in 1951, but never finished it. (He got boxed into a corner and couldn't find a way out.) He began to construct Double-Crostics right after that and by his junior year at Brooklyn College he had a steady source of income flowing in by producing Double-Crostics for a variety of magazines. He continues to supply Double-Crostics today, primarily to Dell Publishing Company.

In 1954 he made another attempt at crosswords with a "literary" 15 × 15. He "followed the *Times* style and used nondictionary type clues whenever possible" and sent it to Margaret Farrar. She rejected it but softened the blow by writing, "I can see you will someday wind up in our puzzle corner, but . . ." Taub "had too many weird 'crosswordese' words, including two that crossed, 'Djos' and 'Oonts.' " Farrar explained that "Djos and Oonts are best avoided altogether, let alone crossing each other."

Following Farrar's advice, Taub soon saw his first crossword in the *Times*. He credits Farrar as the most influential person in his crossword career: "She showed me right from wrong and encouraged me. She kept me honest and on my toes."

Soon after his first crossword was published Taub learned how to solve puns and anagrams puzzles from a "genius type" friend of his who was solving one on the beach. After learning the "solving rules" Taub constructed a few and sent them to Farrar. He drifted toward this style at just the right time for many of Farrar's regular suppliers had died, disappeared, or discontinued creating puns and anagrams and her supplies were dwindling. She started to depend on Taub's contributions and for many years he was the main supplier of puns and anagrams for the *Times*.

Taub didn't actually meet Farrar until 1966, about a dozen years after he had started to construct for her. He and his wife, Phyllis, scheduled a lunch date with Farrar at Sardi's, after overriding her suggestion that they eat in the *Times* cafeteria. Mel and Phyllis didn't know that their lunch hour coincided with Farrar's breakfast hour, but after she ordered an omelet she told them of her nocturnal habits.

Taub's "real career" is as an executive for an insurance company, but his fast-talking manner, charm, and kinetic energy make him ideally suited for the position he holds as the puns-and-anagrams maven of this country. At any gathering of puzzlers Taub stands out with his jokes, deprecating manner, and speedy retorts. Even his traditional crosswords reflect his witty style:

Nasal congestion	Cold storage
Salad ingredient on the *Titanic*	Iceberg lettuce
Conservative Asian	Old school Thai
The mouths of babes	Rattletraps
More than a tun	Over a barrel
Max's blood brother	RH Factor
A waist of time	Hourglass figure

Taub's crossword career has covered such a broad spectrum that it's hard for him to find one specific moment that stands out. When pressed, he admits to feeling happiest when his first book of puns and anagrams appeared in bookstores in 1969. He sums up the overall effect of puzzles on his life this way: "It provided me with a stimulating hobby, a little extra money, a bit of celebrity, and a number of new friends and acquaintances."

PUNS AND ANAGRAMS by Mel Taub

(*SEE PAGE 267 FOR SOLUTION*)

ACROSS

1 Pets found in mom's beds?
8 Decides to miss 50 lbs.
13 This term ain't used for easygoing boss
14 They rise to debate Labourites
16 What Victor said was crude
17 Surest color
18 Makes a mess. OK?
19 Trained ten to go on foray
21 'Taint ma
22 Eros comes back mad
23 Descendant of Cain?
24 Money, but not lira
25 Poll finisher
26 Father may caress 'er
28 Any big toot
29 Reacts to her kiss
31 Angered
33 Tries out riskiest way to go downhill
34 One helluva time
35 Gift forwarded beforehand?
39 They put coating on stapler
43 Puzzle concerning public transportation
44 Manage a lewd one
46 Feline ado from meadow
47 Indian who got land from Toledoan
48 He had Hope's blessing, no less
49 Pro follower
50 He's the opposite of lout
51 Bench from which judge may prohibit 100
52 With first lady, Mr Sparks got squared away
54 Is prayer nothing? No, sir!
56 Too young to need a rug
58 Manages to make tons, e.g.
59 What an idea—star shines!
60 Look at manuscript, briefly
61 He's all rest on the highway

DOWN

1 A hot, 3,000 lb. creature
2 Gunsmith with a rarer M.O.
3 Post for Keats
4 Follower of C?
5 Quite a load, entre nous
6 Kind of race
7 Old novelist Ernest
8 Rita's groove
9 When old you get this way
10 First center for taxpayers
11 Not here to croon off-key?
12 Notice Patti in the ooze?
13 In U.S., Sims' spouse is so called
15 Lasted too long
20 Sounds like one who hurts, in a measure
23 Kind of elf
24 Mirthful, in art
26 Dogs at their summits?
27 Similar to keeping Berg from breaking
28 Good or bad, it's wide
30 What publisher uses, I gather
32 Girl below par
35 Introduction in favor of captain's record?
36 Concerning radials?
37 One bite of this could ruin teeth
38 T' come out ahead
39 P, for example
40 Rise to eat? Amen!
41 Greener bridge player
42 On Wednesdays, Andy goes with them
45 Is liable to find fashionable mutts?
48 Prohibitts? Forbidds?
49 Wild flare
51 Shout disapproval to 1,000?
52 Dead literature
53 It hides look of evil
55 The way Matisse winds up
57 He's against a G.I.'s leave

BARRY TUNICK AND SYLVIA BURSZTYN

BARRY TUNICK, a high-school English teacher, and Sylvia Bursztyn, a legal secretary, team up to create the crosswords for their hometown newspaper, the *Los Angeles Times Magazine*. Bursztyn is responsible for filling the words into the grid and Tunick does all the cluing.

Unlike other crossword teams, they work independently of one another and rarely meet. They use about twenty-five to thirty stock grids, each of which is numbered. After Bursztyn fills in the grid, she telephones Tunick and tells him which grid she's used. He gets out a blank copy and she dictates the words to him as he places them in the grid. Tunick, using a word processor, then clues the puzzle.

He makes four copies of the clues and distributes them to Bursztyn and two proofreaders (along with a copy of the grid), while keeping a copy for himself. Each proofreader solves the puzzle and returns it to Tunick with questions, problems, and/or comments. Bursztyn and Tunick then discuss the changes they wish to make and do any fine-tuning necessary to smooth out the puzzle.

Tunick turns out a clean copy of the clues on his word processor and takes all the materials to a printer who typesets the clues and diagrams and pastes them up. Bursztyn and Tunick each solve the puzzle a last time and make any needed corrections. Then a clean camera-ready crossword is ready to be printed.

They go through this process for each puzzle they create and usually hand in four or five at a time to the paper. As of this writing they've published almost four hundred consecutive crosswords for the *L.A. Times*.

Their partnership began in an unusual way. Tunick had been constructing variety-type quotation puzzles for the *L.A. Times* book-review section when the editor decided that he wanted an exclusive crossword for his section—the syndicated crossword he had been using turned up in other newspapers within his circulation area. Thus his readers were getting the same crossword in two or more newspapers.

The editor asked Tunick to devise a more "literary" puzzle for his section and Tunick obliged with a cryptic crossword. The reaction to it was so negative—three thousand people protested—that Tunick quickly came up with a "regular" crossword.

Tunick didn't feel he had the time to take on this weekly responsibility alone so he looked around for a partner. He found it in Bursztyn, a fellow National Puzzlers' League member and a resident of L.A. They had never met or even corresponded when Tunick contacted her and asked her to collaborate on the crossword. He sought her out because he rightly assumed that she'd be interested in puzzles if she was an NPL member.

Although the modern NPL conventions started in 1976, Tunick didn't start attending until 1984. He's a tall, pleasant man in his late forties. By his own description he's an unemotional person and lives a very ordered life. Bursztyn is a very private person and wishes to remain so. She doesn't attend crossword competitions, NPL conventions, or mini-puzzle gatherings.

Privacy is easy to maintain in the puzzle world for it's probably the most low-keyed division in the publishing field—there isn't a lot of glamour, hoopla, or money involved. Tunick addressed the issue of constructors' pay in the April 1986 edition of *The Crossworder's Own Newsletter.* He noted that the $100 commonly paid for a 21 × 21 crossword could represent more than ten hours of work. This figure "includes developing a theme, entering words, defining, checking definitions, typing, retyping, proofreading, drawing grids, and corresponding with editors." While Tunick didn't have any ready answers for this problem he did open up the issue for future discussion. The low pay doesn't stop Tunick from constructing, but he would, of course, like to see the rates raised.

The puzzles that Tunick and Bursztyn create are almost always themed. They like to use clever twists and wordplay and try to always amuse the solver. Here are some examples from their work.

From "Nicholas Names":

Resoluteness?	William power
Preppie's shoe?	Penelope loafers
Quail?	Robert white

Unfair district division?	Geraldine mander
Muscular strain?	Charles horse
Nursery rhyme opener?	Patricia cake
Seasickness in France?	Malcolm de mer

From "Body Language":

Suffer the consequences	Face the music
Salesperson's toehold	Foot in the door
Pirate find	Treasure chest
Highway warning	Soft shoulder
Foe of 007	Goldfinger
Stars in Vegas	Headliners

From "Misguided Tour":

I don't see any *bagpipers*	Glasgow Kentucky
But my ticket says *USSR*	Moscow Idaho
But where are the *colleens*	Dublin Texas

From "Dropping Out":

No show!	The greatest on earth
No sweat!	Blood and tears
No way!	Rub the wrong
No cover!	The waterfront
No more!	Quoth the raven never

Tunick and Bursztyn also like to give new definitions to common expressions, e.g.:

Exchange dentures?	Switch plates
Woo newscaster?	Court reporter
Redirect signal?	Turn indicator
Follow discs?	Track records
Pull Indy cars?	Drag racers
Polish exhibition sites?	Wax museums
Exhibit humans?	Show people

Tunick's puzzle activities began when he was nine years old and filled in a few blanks in the puzzles his father solved in *The New York Herald Tribune*. He didn't get "hooked" on crosswords until the early sixties when he was working in Nigeria and bought a copy of the London *Daily Telegraph* Crossword collections. Through trial and error (mostly error) he solved the cryptics in that collection. Along the way he "learned a lot about British sports, the military, and college tennis." He never finished a cryptic in those days and after about six months of intermittent solving he had only managed to complete about 30 percent of the book.

In subsequent years he not only learned to solve cryptics but became quite adept at creating them. His anagram clues reflect his love of wordplay:

Arctic Alp hammer is useful	Practical
Convertible Baltic roe mix	Cabriolet
Rot might make me wild	Mildew

While Tunick remains a devotee and composer of cryptics, he recognizes that they are not wildly popular with all segments of the population. He estimates the number of solvers of cryptics to be fewer than forty thousand people. And his experience with the two cryptics he published in the *L.A. Times* seems to support his theory. Tunick was surprised at the hostility his cryptics generated. "I was the most hated man around when I did that," he reminisced. Solvers called and threatened everything from canceling their subscriptions to inflicting bodily harm on the constructor.

Tunick didn't allow that inauspicious beginning to deter him. In addition to the weekly *L.A. Times* puzzle, he constructs double crostics for *Saturday Review* and regular crosswords for specialized magazines like *Good Food, Chevy Camper,* and *Hawaii.*

When he and Bursztyn started their weekly puzzle they "were the interlopers." Now that their puzzle is established, with an estimated audience of 250,000, people "don't complain as much." They "used to get more mail from grumpy people" who wanted them "to stop being so cute."

Now the reactions they get are almost always positive. Fan letters arrive regularly with comments like this: "Thank you for consistently providing such challenging entertainment."

However, fans are quick to notice mistakes which, unfortunately, do from time to time occur. Solvers seem to take a special joy in pointing out errors to constructors. One *L.A. Times* solver carried his "indignation" to new heights on an occasion when 29 Across was mislabeled as 28 Across. He wrote: "I am shocked and outraged that the 29 Across clue was omitted from the March

23 crossword. My lawyers will be contacting your lawyers re the great mental stress and emotional trauma that you have thereby caused me. At the least we are anticipating a $3 million judgment."

Tunick and Bursztyn replied fittingly:

ITER, ATEN, AGORA, STOA AND PROA

ATTORNEYS TO THE CROSSWORD TRADE

CENTURY CITY, CALIFORNIA

Dear——:

We can readily understand your indignation at the apparent omission of 29 Across from the March 23 Puzzler (a typo caused it to be labeled 28 Across). From the flood of lawsuits crossing our desks (including a class action suit filed by Puzpirg, a Ralph Nader organization), your pain and suffering were not unique.

Unfortunately, the issue has been rendered moot by Mr. Tunick's taking the only honorable way out under the circumstances. Yes, he impaled himself on his word processor (no mean feat), leaving as his only tangible asset a pile of black and white squares and a tattered 99¢ dictionary. In the traditional manner he was buried 6 Down and 3 Across.

We understand that his place at *The Times* will be taken by someone else with the same name.

Signed,
Ashe, Ore, Adit, Jr. Partners

PURLOINED LETTERS by Barry Tunick and Sylvia Bursztyn

(SEE PAGE 267 FOR SOLUTION)

ACROSS

1 Modern art?
4 Horse trade
8 Overwrought
13 "Fore!," e.g.
16 Sea inlet
17 Specter
18 *Big Chill*'s Williams
19 Muslim sect
20 Pleased pols
21 No strings
23 Asta's co-owner
24 Frolics
26 ". . . and —— grow on"
27 Dexterity
29 Takes to the 34 Across
30 Makes fast
31 Hood
32 Klutz's comment
33 Attention centers
34 Class dance
35 Swamp stuff
38 Devilkin
39 No Chance
43 Pay dirt
44 Treats unfairly
46 The Obringa, today
47 Synonym lister
48 Raven maven
49 Germanic inscriptions
50 Milan moola
51 Like wet hens
52 Freud's forte
54 Cuban coin
55 Mendelssohn oratorio
59 "I'm Not ——"
60 No end!
64 Darling dog
65 Father Time prop
67 North Carolina college
68 Burnett's co-star
70 Suffered from
71 Nabokov name
72 "Frankly, my dear, I don't —— . . ."
73 Japanese apricot
74 Expanse
77 Dodgertown beach
78 Enrages
79 Ready follower
80 No lie
83 Monk's title
84 Pro vote
85 Fictional Jane
86 Screen's Schneider
87 Hee-haw
89 Where port is left?
90 Stone slab
92 Progress
95 Ecstasy
97 Precipitous
98 The "old" dance
99 Churl
100 No more
103 Ret. account
104 "For —— is a kind of praise"
105 After 90 Down, film Hercules
106 Frightening
107 Teetotalers, for short
108 Green gadget
109 Ant, once
110 Teen woe
111 Take tiffin

DOWN

1 Originate
2 Bowling green areas
3 No go
4 Blows a fuse
5 Rides shank's mare
6 Puts two and two together
7 Favorite
8 Gloomed
9 Borders
10 Wolfe of 35th St.
11 TGIF part
12 *Uncle Vanya* creator
13 In the mode
14 *Casablanca* café owner
15 Chatter
17 Spiffy
18 Winston's mother
19 Pulled thread
22 Hunter's call
25 Chicago area
28 3, e.g.
30 Big Ben sounds
31 Birch or beech
33 Crème de la crème
34 Opening
35 Flavor intensifier: abbr.
36 Salt Lake City pro
37 Complete i's
38 Mordant
39 Mann's Kröger
40 Worried grape?
41 Fortune-teller's deck
42 Presidential impeachment figure Pete
43 Librans' birthstones
44 Twisted
45 Oxidized
50 Duran Duran's Simon
51 Corporate combo
53 Turner's tools
54 Thessaly mountain
56 No sale
57 Red cell shortage
58 Oda occupants
61 Matisse
62 Model of the 60s

63 Overhangs
66 Unlucky
69 Accelerator
71 Le Moko or Le Pew
72 Dwarf
74 Roguish
75 Tiny
76 Zeta-theta separator
77 Miles of film
78 Comden and Green's Green
81 Unsightly blight
82 Hails
83 Hula hoops and pet rocks
87 Previously
88 Run-down
89 Vivacious
90 See 105 Across
91 Doctrine
92 Chengchow's province
93 Main artery
94 It's used to raise dough
95 Tibia or fibula
96 O for McEnroe
97 Goblet part
98 Stokely Carmichael's org.
99 Hazard
101 ID option
102 Free-bird link

WILL WENG

WILL WENG DOESN'T LIKE to see a blank crossword in a newspaper—he thinks it's a "great waste" when the diagram hasn't even been partially filled in by a solver. As puzzle editor of *The New York Times* from 1969 to 1977, Weng edited more than three thousand puzzles that millions of people took a stab at on weekdays, weekends, and holidays. During his tenure at the *Times,* constructors found him to be an editor who firmly believed that solvers shouldn't "expect puzzles to teach [them] anything. They are for pleasure only."

Margaret Farrar, in a preface to the fiftieth anniversary book in the Simon & Schuster series, wrote, "Outrageous puns may be credited . . . to Will Weng himself." He was the perfect editor to expand on fresh concepts. During his tenure, solvers saw puzzles with Arabic numbers ("76 trombones"), Roman numerals ("Life begins at XL"), musical symbols (Becky #); and rebus clues ("AVI" for "Center of gravity").

Weng's innovations weren't limited to the definitions; he allowed liberties to be taken with the diagram itself. One of the most unusual puzzles to appear in the *Times* was one in which one extra square was appended to the top of the grid. The answer read "Sticks out like a sore thumb." His assistant, Harriett Wilson, thought he "had violated a canon of crossword law" with this puzzle, but there were no frantic calls or poison-pen letters from solvers about this puzzle.

Weng did hear from solvers, however, whenever he made a mistake. He learned that "some people . . . not only are willing to fritter their time away with the daily and Sunday puzzles but often are in deadly earnest about what appears in them" and that there was "always a rotten apple in the barrel ready to pounce on some little thing."

Weng heard from a "churlish purist in Princeton" when he clued "tepee" as "Home for Powhatan." The solver pointed out that only Plains Indians in the West lived in tepees and Powhatan as a Delaware Indian didn't fit into that category.

"Some demon on Long Island" corrected Weng when he used

the clue, "His first capital was Springfield" for "Abraham Lincoln." This solver pointed out that Springfield wasn't yet the capital of Illinois when Lincoln was first elected to the Illinois legislature.

A ten-year-old "dedicated follower of the Pittsburgh Pirates" corrected Weng when he clued "Bob Veale" as a "National League pitcher." David Wallace of New York wrote that Veale "was traded to the Boston Red Sox, thus making him an American League pitcher." To substantiate his claim, Wallace sent Weng his baseball card of Veale wearing a Boston uniform.

Since Wallace's rebuke was printed in the *Times,* Weng had an opportunity to reply publicly: "When I was 10 years old baseball players stayed in their own league, or so I recall dimly. Nowadays you have to read the fine print to keep up with the shuttle service between the National and American Leagues."

Weng used myriad references for his editorial research. Sometimes he had to read an entire book to verify a fact. When he clued "Never Never Land" as "Locale for Peter Pan" he heard from a solver who informed him that there was only one "Never" in Peter Pan's land. Weng recalls, "I hadn't read the book, but I was so sure I was right that I got a copy of the book and read it. And never, never was I so wrong."

"In the line of duty" Weng reread *The Hound of the Baskervilles*. He wanted to link the word "mastiff" with the book and "felt positive that the *Baskervilles* hound was a mastiff." He pored through the two-hundred-page book and didn't find a mastiff. But he "did enjoy a good mystery."

Weng's early background helped to prepare him for his future career. He nurtured his love of words and word games during his childhood with the puzzles in *Saint Nicholas* and *American Boy* magazine. But in late adolescence he was one of the few people who didn't get wholly involved in the crossword craze. He was seventeen when the first crossword book was published, but "couldn't get to first base" with the puzzles in it.

It was in the 1930s that Weng began solving the crosswords in *The New York Herald Tribune*. In 1931, he joined the news staff of *The New York Times*. Hired as a reporter, he was transferred to the copy desk. During World War II he censored press dispatches for the navy, first in New York and then in Pearl Harbor and Guam.

After the war, Weng returned to the *Times* and eventually became the head of the Metropolitan copy desk, a position he held for fifteen years. He started to construct crosswords in the fifties and sent them to Margaret Farrar through the interoffice mail.

Weng's first Sunday crossword in the *Times* featured vaudeville style jokes:

Lament of a landlocked mariner	Long time no sea
Penalty for bigamy	Two mothers-in-law

Weng's "The Pun's the Thing" crossword in 1967 broke new ground in the *Times,* for it was the first punny Sunday crossword. Clues included:

Large, tiresome animals	Colossal boars
Subway for Bugs Bunny, perhaps	Rabbit transit
Summonses to a dessert	Mousse calls
Rodent's cussword	Beaver damn
Where some animals play golf	Public lynx
What author Virginia got as a girl	Woolf whistles

Two years after Weng's punny crossword was published, Margaret Farrar retired and the *Times* offered him the crossword editor's job. Reflecting on his early days in that position, Weng wrote in an article for the *Four-Star Puzzler* in 1982: "When I first took over the job as crossword-puzzle editor of *The New York Times* I put the first puzzle in front of me, looked at it helplessly, and then asked myself, 'What do I do now?' The puzzle itself looked all right and the definitions seemed fully adequate. So apparently all I had to do was check out a few spellings and basic facts, and I'd be in business. But I had a feeling it wasn't quite that simple."

In an interview in *Writer's Digest,* Weng said that crossword-puzzle editing is mostly "working on the definitions. Changing and sharpening up, checking for accuracy—I have to go to the dictionary all the time. By and large I find there is quite a bit of changing done in definitions and in the puzzles themselves. . . . [I change words] to try to get away from what I consider to be awkward combinations or something I can't find in the dictionary. I try to have everything in the clues come from a standard reference source."

Weng's refreshing clues enlivened many of the puzzles he edited. Some of his specialties include:

Tailless game animal	Donkey
City of great recall	Detroit
Large brass container	Pentagon
Useful picnic intruder	Aardvark

When *Writer's Digest* asked Weng, "What are the problem areas of puzzlemaking?" he replied: "You have to find them for yourself. You have to put your long entries down first and then tentatively set a pattern around your long key entries. And you have to always be symmetrical in the pattern. One letter too many in one place will ruin a design and mean changes of words to keep the design. Then you may have to juggle a black square here and there or change a word. But once the puzzle is pretty well formed you have to watch as you put in words to see where new trouble is going to lie. For instance, an R and a Q next to each other is a red flag that you'd better know what you are going to do before you continue making the puzzle."

Weng's mandatory retirement from the *Times* in 1977 elicited a flood of mail. Most solvers thanked him for "eight years of perfectly splendid puzzles." Eli Wallach, an actor whose name frequently appears in crosswords, thanked Weng for "the wonderful eight years . . . as puzzle editor." He went on to say what crosswords meant to him: "I never ceased to be excited when I saw: 34 Across, Actor —— Wallach. My name used to leap out of the page. It also put me in a hallowed class with Whitney and Yale, and, even at times, a Biblical prophet."

Logo for Will Weng's Crosswords Club

Since his retirement, Weng has continued to edit the *Times* crossword series books. In 1982 he embarked on a new venture, The Crosswords Club. The concept of offering club members four brand-new puzzles every month was dreamed up by Nob Hovde and Jonas Gold, two advertising professionals who wanted to "bring Will Weng out of retirement." Hovde and Gold approached Weng with their idea and he agreed to give it a try.

Weng's fans were sufficiently motivated by the advertising to join the club in record numbers. Every month club members receive "four puzzles freshly edited" by Weng. "These puzzles, developed exclusively for members of the . . . club, are of the size and caliber of the vintage Sunday puzzles edited by" Weng.

Puzzles, created by some of the top constructors in the country, are printed on quality stock. Each one is themed and "contains the solution to the preceding Weng-of-the-Week, and . . . a commentary by" Weng.

Weng's commentaries can provide more information about a clue or can be an interesting piece of puzzle history. He elaborated on the answer word "Puff" by describing him as "a dragon who lived in a land called Honalee. He was immortalized in a song by Peter, Paul and Mary."

Re the entry "R. E. Lee" Weng remarked that this "would have been unthinkable in the early, unimaginative days of the crossword puzzle. But a crusading editor, Margaret Farrar, expanded the puzzle to allow the use of word combinations and phrases, and in the process added to the zest of solving. Some people still object to the use of phrases or gimmicks, but the majority seem to find that they add an interesting and challenging new dimension."

When choosing the puzzles for the club Weng looks for clever themes and clues. As he edits he doesn't "strain" to make the clues punny or funny, but they have the Weng touch:

Transaction of interest	Loan
They're often not included	Batteries

His "Funny Business" crossword for the 1986 Stamford Marriott Tournament contained "some office talk that's offered all in pun":

Tales of business derring do?	Charge accounts
Party food provided by the staff?	Secretarial spread
A chocolate for the boss?	Executive sweet

Weng doesn't have to be punny to be creative. In "Measure for Measure" the theme was "law" presented in an unusual manner:

Oddsmaker's enactment?	Law of averages
What Leo enforces?	Law of the jungle
Commands for eatery cooks	Short orders
Precept on employee incompetence	Peter Principle
Place a statute on the table?	Lay down the law
Hand-y statute?	Rule of thumb
Powerful family member	Mother-in-law
Dictates from above	Act of God

In "Franchise Wise" the voting theme was a little more subtle than his punny themes:

November stuffings	Ballot boxes
Place of solitary confinement	Voting booth
Reagan's plea to the populace?	Elect Ron
People created in November?	Ins and outs
He goes to de polls!	Devoter

Before Weng left the *Times* he wrote a farewell column in which he said, "One can hardly call eight years as a puzzle editor much of a career. Some might even say that any number of years as a puzzle editor isn't much of a career. But it has seemed like a lifetime to me and I have enjoyed every minute of it."

Weng was feted at an eightieth birthday party in March 1987, hosted by Eugene T. Maleska at a New York City restaurant and attended by seventy-five constructors and editors. Weng, acknowledging his accolades in his droll manner while chomping on a big cigar, looked years younger than his octagenarian status. He was still enjoying every minute.

ON THE ROAD by Will Weng

(SEE PAGE 267 FOR SOLUTION)

ACROSS

1 Door and short
6 Egyptian dam
11 Admiral in the Vichy regime
17 —— Army of golf
19 Larry or Moe
20 Imagines
22 Highway sign
24 Vehicle for instant riches
25 Mortar beater
26 Upstate N.Y. river
27 Highway sign
29 Get —— (start)
31 Law, to Pierre
32 One permanently AWOL
33 Wrap
35 High pool
37 Per ——
38 Lively party
42 Batch of bills
43 Be taxing
44 Power measure: abbr.
45 Nobel chemist 1934
46 Following
49 Mike's friend
50 Traveler's target: abbr.
53 Oleo or butter
55 Of the cloth
57 Place for a coup
58 Small type
59 Stench
60 Writer Hobson
61 Western Indian
62 Star in Pegasus
63 Urban highway sight
67 Greek letters
71 Kentucky grass
73 Ringworm
74 Flower parts
76 With full force
79 Pork cut
80 Gawks
81 Derided
83 Made a rating: abbr.
84 Gym piece
85 Camels' goals
86 From —— (the works)
87 Auto starter: abbr.
89 Kind of pistol
90 State captial V.I.P.
91 Leningrad's river
92 Broadway musical
94 Northern native
95 Fencing pieces
98 Burlesque performer
100 Attila follower
102 Filberts and pistachios
104 Highway sign
108 Curtain material
110 Humorist Bill
111 Divide proportionately
112 Highway sign
115 Small stalk
116 Plaza girl
117 Placed at intervals
118 Mounts
119 Medicinal plant
120 Gives backing to

DOWN

1 Native Israeli
2 Handles
3 Half a quarter, formerly
4 Moslem saint
5 Paving stone
6 Aleutian island
7 Large tub of old
8 Expressionless
9 Chills
10 Cleared
11 Makes watery
12 "Venite ——" (Yule song words)
13 Do a paving job
14 Plaster backing
15 Suit to ——
16 River to the Tiber
18 Smirched
19 Like an arrow
21 A Chaplin son
23 In addition
28 Kind of rug
30 Cutesy highway sign
32 Help with the dishes
34 Member of the gull family
36 Louvre offering
38 Highway sign
39 Space
40 N.Y.S.E. membership
41 London park
46 Peak
47 Piece of pastry
48 Low-caste Hindu
49 One of Henry's wives
50 Street sign
51 Stove, in Naples
52 Old Sicilian coin
54 Way to stand
56 Hip joint
60 Opposite of fortis
61 Annapolis initials
64 One of seven
65 Spanish relatives
66 First N.T. book
68 Rudolph or Myra
69 Early English moneys
70 J.F.K. visitors
72 —— for the road

75 Scout unit
76 Island off Donegal
77 Word with play or check
78 Black Sea arm
80 It's often starred
82 Used a steno's services
84 Motorist's aid
88 Ring stones
89 Auto
90 Large jibs
93 Skyline units
94 "Let that be a —— to you"
96 A Shriver
97 Pointed instrument
98 Climb
99 English dramatist George
101 French article
103 Bird food
104 Document certifiers: abbr.
105 Leavings
106 Dutch measure
107 French weapon
108 Shuttle mover
109 Asian palm
113 Kind of horn
114 Fairy queen

CONSTRUCTING CROSSWORDS

Crosswords conform to several general rules:

The diagram must be symmetrical. For every four-letter word in the top left corner, there must be four-letter word in the bottom right corner. The diagram will look the same if it's turned upside down.

All words must interlock with each other; each letter in the grid is part of both an across and a down word.

No two-letter words are permitted; three-letter words should be used sparingly.

Each entry in the grid must be a "real" word or a legitimate phrase, capable of being found in some reference source. There must be no "forced entries."

Though each constructor profiled here goes about the creative process in a unique way, here are some general rule-of-thumb directions:

First, think of a theme. Collect as many words or phrases related to the theme and organize them in lists according to word length so that they can be entered symmetrically in the grid.

Second, plot a pattern of black squares on a blank grid. Use graph paper or make up your own grids in standard crossword sizes, e.g., 15 squares by 15 squares, 17 by 17, 21 by 21. Place the black squares in the grid in such a way that there are no unkeyed letters.

Third, start placing words in the grid. Begin with the spots that are most likely to give you trouble and work toward the easier spots. Most editors have maximum word counts permissible in each direction for each size puzzle. These range from 76 to 80 words for a 15 × 15 and from 138 to 140 for a 21 × 21.

Fourth, write your clues. Try to be witty and look at words from new angles. In *The Compleat Cruciverbalist,* authors Stan Kurzban and Mel Rosen present a sampling of the ways "tree" can be clued: "oak or elm," "banyan, for instance," "corner," "stretch shoes," "Kilmer's symbol of beauty," "surgeon of a sort," "type of frog," "family, for one," "forest feature," "leopard's perch," "picnic umbrella" and "da digit afta two."

Fifth, number the grid. Place a numeral in each white square across the top row and then number the beginning of each across and down word.

Sixth, type the clues and redo the diagram neatly. If mailing the puzzle to an editor for possible publication, prepare two identical grids—one blank one and one with the letters filled in.

Some constructors started out by using already published grids and filling them in with their own words. This is a valid way to begin if you've never made a crossword before. But you have much more flexibility if you create your own grid.

Write to the editors of all the puzzle magazines and ask them for their style sheets. Always include a self-addressed, stamped envelope with all correspondence.

CROSSWORD CONTESTS

CROSSWORD SOLVING IS a solitary pursuit, performed behind the privacy of one's newspaper or in the confines of one's home. At crossword tournaments, however, solvers compete openly in a public area for cash prizes. The lure behind the contests, though, goes far beyond monetary reward.

For veteran contestant Judy Wolff, a systems manager from Acton, Massachusetts, the draw is camaraderie: "I'm not one of the stars who finishes in the top ten. I typically rank in the top twenty-five percent, but that's many points away from first place. I always try to have fun, talk to people, visit with old friends and make new friends. I really enjoy the camaraderie at these tournaments. The participants are all bright, friendly, interesting people. You don't have to win a trophy to come home happy from these tournaments. I treasure every moment of fun and friendship I've had at these weekends and have many personal memories of each one."

The modern era of crossword contests began in March 1978 with the Stamford Marriott competition. Subsequently, there have been more than thirty events—some are small, low-keyed contests, primarily for local residents; others are highly competitive, attracting contestants from across the country.

The annual Marriott tournament is one example of the latter. Every year many of the same contestants—students, housewives, business executives, accountants, writers, teachers, computer programmers, and stock brokers—return to Stamford, Connecticut, to test their skills against their peers, meet people with similar interests, solve exceptional puzzles, and have fun.

Contestants know that coordinator Will Shortz will commission creative puzzles from top constructors and that his team of judges will mark the puzzles correctly and post the standings on time.

The contests are also appealing for the sheer beauty of the crosswords themselves and the unusual ambience of solving en masse. Tournament crosswords, printed on quality stock with bold lettering, offer an esthetic allure not found in crosswords in daily newspapers. Moreover, the sound of hundreds of pencils filling in the blanks in an otherwise intensely quiet auditorium quickens solvers' adrenaline and gives an impetus that just doesn't exist when one solves solo behind a newspaper.

In a crossword competition speed and accuracy are stressed. Contests consist of a predetermined number of solving rounds, with time limits ranging from fifteen to forty-five minutes. Contestants earn 10 points for every correct word entered across and down; 25 points for each full minute they finish before the time limit, and 150 bonus points for a perfect paper. Often the top contestants complete the lead-off puzzle (a 15×15) in four to five minutes and the final puzzle (a 21×21) in eleven to twelve minutes.

Referees collect the puzzles as they're completed and indicate the number of bonus minutes earned. Judges, working in a separate area, mark each paper, noting the number of words and letters missed. All this information is fed into a computer program designed by Mike Shenk. After the six rounds on Saturday the contestants are ranked in order from first to last and the standings are posted early Sunday morning, prior to the seventh round. The seventh round becomes crucial for all contestants in the top ten positions, for a super score in this round can radically alter one's standing.

After the seventh round the three highest-scoring contestants participate in a sudden-death playoff. They solve a puzzle on large Plexiglas grids on stage, in full view of the other contestants, judges, guests, and the media, with all mistakes being recorded for posterity. Clues in the final puzzle are devious, clever, and challenging:

I will usually follow them	EFGH
Figurehead	CPA
One way to get information	Dial 0
Bow deeply	Scrape a leg
More than asleep	In a coma
Sunday player	Organist
Lightweight boxer?	Pup

The winner is the contestant who finishes the final puzzle in the shortest amount of time with the fewest errors. Judging is done on the spot and the winner is announced immediately. Prizes are awarded a few hours later at a banquet luncheon.

Contestants, separated by dividers, solving crosswords during a Marriott tournament. Contestants concentrate on solving the puzzles as rapidly and accurately as possible.

Contestants relax in the lobby of the Stamford Marriott Hotel between solving rounds. Many of them pass the time by solving crosswords.

Mike Shenk devised a computer program for scoring and ranking solvers' puzzles. He and his computer travel to most of the major competitions.

Judges Henry Hook, Stephanie Abrams-Hook, Douglas Heller, Helene Hovanec, and Stan Newman watch Mike Shenk punch out the rankings on the computer.

The judges—most of whom are editors or constructors—have developed a comfortable working relationship. Some of them see each other only at the Stamford tournament and use that time to catch up on each other's lives and trade shop talk. Meal conversations are peppered with outrageous puns as they devise punny clues for hypothetical crosswords. At the 1986 contest the group compiled a list of song titles based on cars—"Toyota Be in Pictures," "Honda Road Again," "Old Volks at Home," "Ferrari We Know" and "Secondhand Rolls."

Solvers feel the same warmth about the competition. Since 1978 Jay Kasofsky has spent the first weekend in March with lawyer Marilyn Munro. Says Kasofsky, a high-school history teacher from Woodridge, New York: "There are a few contestants who evoke the aspect of *Same Time Next Year*. I feel a kinship established over the years—no pretenses, no facades, easy to be myself—that I don't have with many people I've known all my life."

Games magazine ran its own contest for five years. Dubbed the U.S. Open, it began innocently every year with a qualifying puzzle in its March issue. Successful solvers then received four tie-breaker puzzles commissioned by Shortz from constructors whose names he never revealed (to protect them from irate solvers) to weed out weaker wordsmiths. Clues included puns:

Why the amnesiac bought a sweat suit	To jog his memory
Ski races	Slalom occasions
Chef's Valentine	A hug and a quiche

and obscure definitions:

Underwool of the musk ox	Quiviut
Part of a riyal	Qursh

and devious definitions:

It goes with four or six, but not three or five	Teen
Green acres	Ireland
Tense moment	Present

Although the clues got more convoluted each year, thousands of solvers continued to vie for the 250 slots available at the one-day contest, held in August in New York City. Some contestants even managed to solve all four tie breakers correctly. One year, a few of these achievers printed up special T-shirts announcing: "I am one of the 17 elite" and wore them to the Open (none of them won). The top prize of $1,500 (plus a six-foot pencil) was the richest in puzzle competitions.

Innovations at the U.S. Open have included auditory and visual cluing. In Mike Shenk's "Hear Ye, Hear Ye" crossword, sounds—Dr. Ruth's voice, a towhee's call, and music by The Platters—were presented orally on tape. In another year, photos of actor Gene Wilder, a jib sail, Alcoa's logo, and other objects replaced written clues.

The other major tournaments are the Presenting Baltimore Inc. Crossword Open (a two-day event held in February) and the North Jersey Crossword Open (a one-day contest that takes place in June), both coordinated by Stan Newman. Rules and prizes are similar to those of the Marriott competition and attract a lot of the same solvers.

Most of the top contestants prepare rigorously for tournaments.

Top solver Ellen Ripstein finished in the money in several contests. Since she is "now expected to perform well" she feels tremendous pressure and trains accordingly:

"I prepare for a tournament the same way an athlete or musician trains—practice! I do every decent puzzle I can find, as many as twenty-five a day during peak training periods. I also practice with other contestants, racing on the same puzzles under tournament conditions. While it helps to know obscure Brazilian birds and Malaysian canoes, I don't make a conscious effort to learn 'crosswordese'; these words become familiar with practice. A skilled constructor avoids obscure words anyway. A good solver needs mental agility, open-mindedness, and a sense of humor. When faced with the definition 'flower,' one must consider both a garden plant and a river."

Advertising executive John Chervokas (creator of Mr. Whipple and "Please don't squeeze the Charmin") and veteran of fifteen contests, frequently places in the top ten. Winner of two Ridgewood Newspaper Tournaments, he is "genetically competitive" and loves to "compete in life." He trains for one week prior to each contest by solving ten puzzles a day and eating a lot of fish, especially lobster.

Winners receive an added bonus in their post-tournament pub-

Third-prize winner Ellen Ripstein solving the playoff puzzle at the Ninth Annual Stamford Marriott contest.

Tournament director Will Shortz (rear left) and the winners of the Ninth Annual Stamford Marriott Tournament—second place winner Rebecca Kornbluh (front left), first place winner David Rosen (front center), third place winner Ellen Ripstein (front right) and fourth place winner Ed Bethea (rear right).

licity. When Miriam Raphael won the 1979 Stamford contest she was a celebrity guest on *To Tell the Truth* and the *Today* show, appeared on local radio shows, collected a scrapbook full of clippings from newspapers around the country, heard from long-lost childhood friends and relatives, and received a congratulatory note from her congressman. She also made a decisive career change.

When Raphael won the contest she was a teacher of English as a second language. After winning several more tournaments she was commissioned by Simon & Schuster to edit a series of crossword books. After that she became an associate editor at Penny Press.

As a result of her triumphs in several crossword contests, Rebecca Kornbluh, a weaver from Mundelein, Illinois, has appeared on the *Today* and Regis Philbin shows and has been the subject of articles in domestic and foreign newspapers. Others regard her as a walking dictionary:

"I get strange phone calls asking for help on a peculiar assortment of problems. One gentleman phoned from Massachusetts to ask for help on a crossword his daughter had to do as a school assignment. And when a Florida paper started carrying a crossword, the features editor called to ask for help because he couldn't solve it. It's not the easiest thing to solve a crossword over the phone!"

The purse at crossword tournaments is minuscule compared to those at athletic events—typically, prizes range from $100 to $400. Contestant Joel Darrow wants to see big-money crossword contests. An investment banker, Darrow is a serious competitor who has entered almost all the modern tournaments, placing in the top twenty most of the time, and winning second and third prizes on several occasions. "The caliber of the best solvers will be fully appreciated only when they get more publicity and much greater rewards. The best pro bowlers win over one hundred thousand dollars a year, the best women golfers twice that. Tennis players, male and female, can make millions each year. The best crossword solver will make perhaps two thousand dollars and buy his own pencils! When the day comes that the best solver takes home twenty thousand dollars from a fifty-thousand-dollar prize pool, for winning one tourney (covered by network television), then crosswords will have arrived. Within the next five years, it could all come true."

STILL A SQUARE DEAL

MILLIONS OF SOLVERS are loyally devoted to a daily crossword in their favorite newspapers, while millions more buy the hundreds of crossword magazines on the market. The crossword is the most popular puzzle of all time. What are the intrinsic features that have enabled it not only to survive but to flourish? There are many opinions:

"Crossword puzzles are insidiously like life. They promise victory at the end. They present mystery at the beginning and along the way."—*Literary Review,* 1924

From the beginning of time people have been "mystically beguiled with words . . . with tricks that can be done with words . . . and with the mysterious relations between words that could be joined in some construction."—MARGARET FARRAR, PROSPER BURANELLI, and F. GREGORY HARTSWICK, *Collier's,* 1925

"Crossword puzzling is the only satisfactory form of solitaire yet devised by the fertile brain of man. The pied pattern of black and white squares is a personal challenge to all that is in you of information, imagination, industry and ingenuity."—*North American Review,* 1929

"Crossword puzzles fill man's need to kill time in a mild and non-neurotic way while we wait—for doctors, dentists, spouses, washing machines to end, trips to end, etc."—EUGENE RACHLIS, *Collier's,* 1955

"People do crossword puzzles for the same reason they become mathematicians and scientists. They know in advance that there is an answer."—DAVID CORT, *The Nation,* 1961

Solving crosswords is an excellent mental exercise because "the pencil-and-paper responses involved are active, not passive, and because those responses exercise our command of the social reality embodied in language. . . . To search one's mind for the right word is not merely a challenge: It is an effort that exercises the mind and corrects our natural tendencies toward forgetfulness and confusion."—ROBERT OLIPHANT, *New York Times,* Op-Ed page, 1980

Any educational value of the crossword puzzle is an ancillary reward for its prime purpose is recreational. People solve for fun.

On December 22, 1918, Arthur Wynne publicly rebuked a teacher who wrote that she encouraged her pupils to solve his puzzles because of their educational value. Her own solving experience had allowed her to become "acquainted with a great many dictionary words" of whose existence she had been unaware. Though flattered by her letter, Wynne made it very clear that puzzles "are to amuse as well as elevate, and to take our minds off war prices, income taxes, the high cost of living, and other disagreeable subjects for a few moments, or maybe hours, each week."

Margaret Farrar was positive that the sales of crossword books rose in severe economic crises for two basic reasons—they were a form of inexpensive recreation and a great escape mechanism.

Humorist Phyllis McGinley described crosswords as "sedative as Nembutal, absorbing as a detective story, more innocent than cigarettes or kisses . . . the perfect mechanism for escape."

Who solves crosswords seems to be as important as why people solve. One of the reasons behind the crossword's early success was that so many of the intellectuals of the twenties adopted the craze. Newspapers were filled with articles about the luminaries—F.P.A., Heywood Broun, Gelett Burgess, Ruth Hale, and Kathleen Norris—who solved and/or constructed crosswords.

On January 13, 1925, *The New York Times* announced: "Queen Mary has taken up the pastime of solving puzzles." Lesser members of the royal family were also known to be "addicted to the word-hunting game." In a follow-up editorial the next day, the *Times* defended royalty's right to solve: "Whatever joys the crossword puzzle can give, royalty has a right to share, and that it is doing so helps to confirm the growing suspicion that the theoretical wearers of crowns are much like other human beings. . . ."

Through the years celebrities—Henry Fonda, Greer Garson, Nancy Olson, Julie Harris, Rex Stout, Mary Roberts Rinehart, Marlene Dietrich, Winston Churchill, Bernard Baruch, and Princess Margaret—were known to be addicted to the black and white grids.

Actress Ellen Burstyn educated herself by reading the encyclopedia and by solving crosswords. In an interview in 1975 she stated: "I may be uneducated but I've got a doctorate in crossword puzzles."

Crosswords were included in the 1974 Gallup poll on sports

and indoor games. Interviewers found that 27 percent of the participants had solved a crossword puzzle in the past year.

Crosswords were on the curriculum two times at the New School for Social Research in New York City. Michael Miller, who was only fourteen when his first crossword was published in the *Times,* taught "Beyond Crossword Puzzles" for two semesters. The course was geared for "competent crossword solvers who wished to expand their puzzle horizons" into such areas as diagramless puzzles and cryptic crosswords. Margaret Farrar, Mel Taub, Will Weng, and Will Shortz were guest speakers at some sessions. Miller was fifteen and seventeen when he taught the courses.

Crossword subtleties and changes aren't noticed by nonsolvers. However, aficionados interject crosswords into areas where they usually don't appear, such as:

- The personals column in a local New Jersey paper—"Divorcee seeks exceptional man who enjoys the arts, sports, travel, good conversation, quiet moments and the Sunday *Times* crossword puzzle."
- The Question and Answer section of the *Times* food section—Question: "I am addicted to crossword puzzles and often find the word 'alec' as the answer to 'a fish sauce.' Are you familiar with this sauce and can it be obtained in bottled form?" Answer: "The word is found only in crossword puzzles and one's chances of finding it at a local store are nil."
- An article about the Bull and Finch Pub in Boston, the model for the TV show *Cheers:* "Dennis Flynn, a regular at the pub, does crosswords at the bar. He got up from the bar to make a phone call leaving behind a carefully folded newspaper and a half-finished puzzle. He returned to find a tourist on his stool, bent over the puzzle, pen in hand. Flynn drained his glass, picked up the newspaper, and crumpled it into a little ball. He stormed out the door."
- A report about the *New York Times* annual shareholders' meeting in *The Wall Street Journal*: Sol Hyman, a shareholder, said the paper's Sunday crossword puzzle is "so tough that most people need all week to solve it."

David Bear found his wife through the *New York Times* crossword. In his article 42ND STREET ACROSS AND MADISON DOWN, pub-

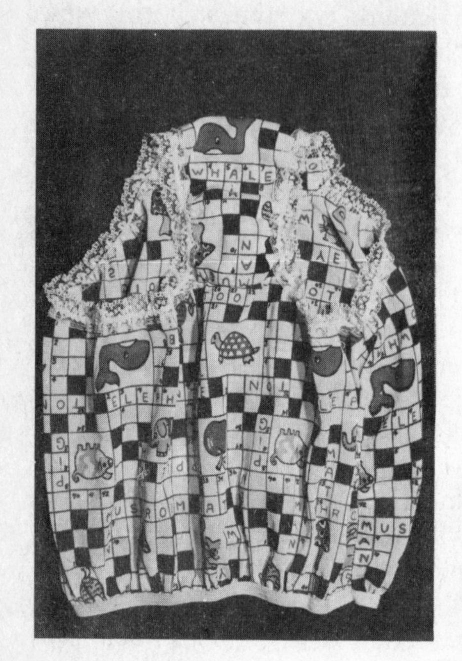

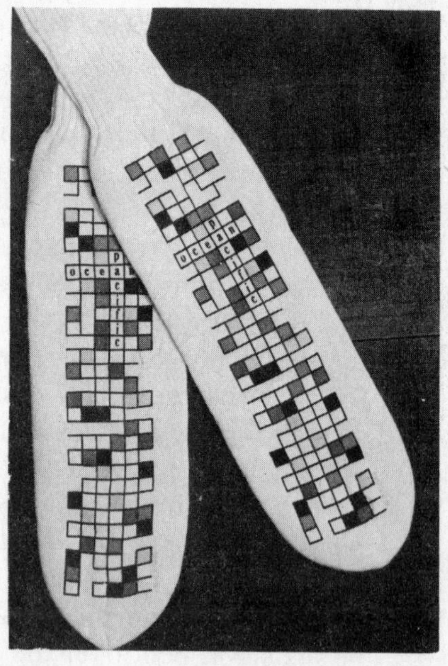

The crossword grid appears in unusual places—on underwear and on socks.

lished in *New York* magazine on May 8, 1978, Bear recounted the events leading up to the proposal. For several months Bear retrieved one particular copy of the *Times* from a trash can on Forty-second Street and got to "know" the owner of the original paper by analyzing his partially completed crosswords. One day Bear met the solver (Walter Crandall) and told him that he had been finishing his crossword puzzles for a few months. After several meetings and chats Crandall invited Bear to his home to meet his family. Bear fell in love with Crandall's oldest daughter and, after a proper courtship, they married. Bear's favorite wedding present was a picture of his wife and him with this caption underneath, "I got my wife through *The New York Times*."

The *Times* puzzle is one of the most widely solved puzzles in the world. Yet it appeared that crosswords would never be deemed "fit to print." In an editorial on November 17, 1924, at the height of the crossword craze, a *Times* editorial stated: "Scarcely recovered from the form of temporary madness that made so many people pay enormous prices for mah jong sets, about the same persons now are committing the same sinful waste in the utterly futile finding of words the letters of which will fit into a pre-arranged pattern, more or less complex. This is not a game at all, and it hardly can be called a sport; it merely is a new utilization of leisure for those for whom it otherwise would be empty and tedious."

PUZZLE ANSWERS

Cinema Subtraction

Grizzly Business

Cryptic Crossword by Cox and Rathvon

ACROSS 1. MINNESOTA (anagram) 6. S(TO)IC 9. SPAGHETTI (anag.) 10. EASE-L 11. DESERT (homophone) 12. CHAP-LAIN 14. VERS(A-ILL)ES 16. OGLE (hidden) 18. G-APE 19. NOVITIATES (anag.) 21. BREA(THE)D 22. DISCUS(s) 26. NI(E)CE 27. HEAR-TACHE (*teach* anag.) 28. SIT-UP (reversal) 29. RES(TRAIN)T

DOWN 1. M-USED 2. NEARS (anag.) 3. ETHE-REAL 4. (g)OATS 5. ARITHMETIC (anag.) 6. S(LEE)PY 7. ONSLAUGHT (anag.) 8. COLANDERS 13. ALT(OGETH)ER (*he got* anag.) 14. VA-GA-BONDS 15. REP-RESENT 17. S(IN)ISTER 20. STREEP (anag.) 23. C(ACT)I 24. S-CENT 25. BASS (double definition)

Cryptic Crossword by Doug and Janis Heller

ACROSS

1 two meanings
4 two meanings
9 anagram (vine mat)
11 "hic" inside "et al."
12 F + I do
13 anagram (the id)
14 two meanings
17 compass ion ate
19 anagram (Hojo plans June)
21 iF I JIggle
22 bra in
23 sounds like "or a"
26 anagram (Ken tuna)
27 anagram (Gain ire)
28 anagram (unit of an)
29 moDEL VErsion

DOWN

1 anagram (safe cave)
2 anagram (fed more)
3 two meanings
5 elect + "or" backward + cut + ion
6 A Che
7 In clued
8 thE CLATter
10 mod USO per and I
15 Lathe
16 Ban Jo
18 "ad" in "escape"
19 "ju(st) ju(st)" around "its"
20 anagram (Real nut)
21 flu + ff
24 anagram (kits)
25 Dega(s)

Bent Seller List

Who's That Again?

HELM FBI COSI OVID
OLIO MIEN OBIT RENO
PERU PLACEBODOMINGO
IVANTHETREBLE EAGER
TIS TEN SPINE
TANYA YASSUHARAFAT
ATOP MISS KNOWS URE
NEWYEAR ELIOT ALMA
KNOTTIER ELP ERG
RHONDAPHLEGMING
ONE HER NUMBERED
ATTN CRASS MASSEUR
DUO AGUAS HIPS MARE
ATTILATHEHON VOTED
AMATI ARS GAR
SELIM COURTESYLEMAY
WILDBILLHICCUP HOLE
INEE SELF UTES ANET
TEDS ASAS TAR TAXI

Diagramless

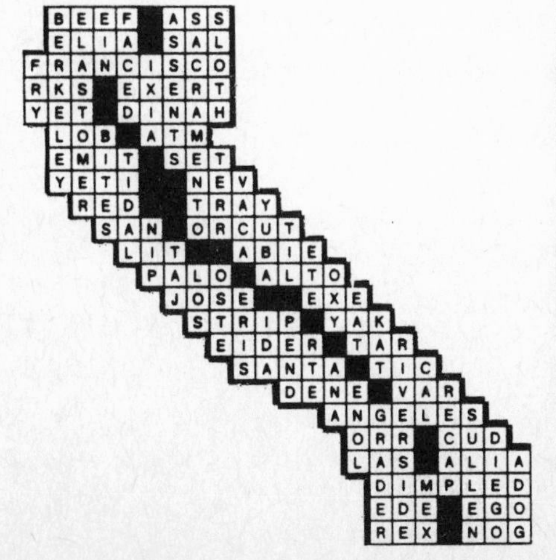

Nines and Fives

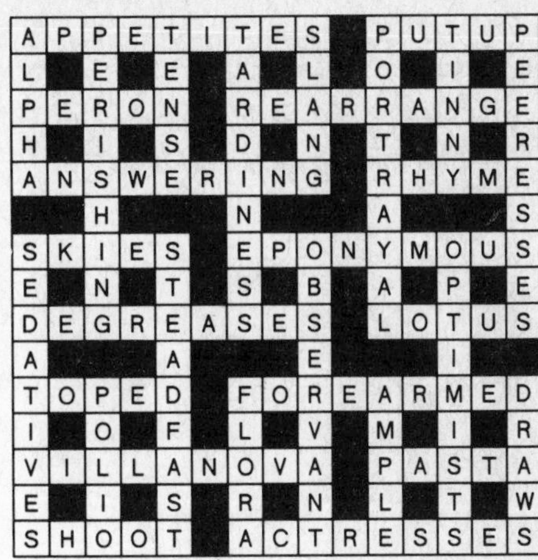

ACROSS

1 A + P + PETITE + S
6 PUT UP (palindrome)
9 PE(R)ON
10 REAR + RANGE
11 A (N,S,W,E) RING
12 "RHYME" (& lit.)
13 SKI(E)S
15 (E)PONY + MOUS~~E~~
18 DEGRE(A + S)ES
19 LOT + US
20 TOPED (rev.)
22 FOR(EAR)MED
25 VI(LLANO)VA
26 PAST + A
27 SHOOT (2 defs.)
28 A + C + TRESSES

DOWN

1 ALP + H + A
2 PER(I)SHING
3 TENSE (hidden)
4 TARDINESS (anag.)
5 S(L)ANG
6 PORT(RAY)AL
7 T + IN + NY
8 P(~~S~~EE~~N~~)RESSES
13 SEDATIVES (anag.)
14 STEAD(F)AST (*sad state* anag.)
16 OB + SERVANT
17 OPT + I + MIS(T)S
21 POL(I)O
22 FL(OR)A
23 ~~S~~AMPLE
24 DRAWS (2 defs.)

Teamwork

SHOO IGLOOS MUG AFRO
PENNANDINGE SISI PROM
CARMENSANDCOHENS PAPA
CREESE MOO BEN MILNER
SAD ORT AWED OPEC
PEWS DIALED STEAM
ORB AILS SHIRR ERASE
LOU URSULAE KNAP ENID
ASTIN TRALA ESCE EDDA
NATASHA TINT TATA NEL
OLEAN ENDIS NEMEA
AWN EDDS ETTE DRIBBLE
SASS ADAM WAROF LOOEY
SNAP TERI INVOICE RTE
ANNES RESAT OLEO SOS
MADAM NEARTO ALVA
BREA WEYS DEM HUB
FOEMEN BAA HAD ROMANO
ALAI STARRSANDSTREEPS
IDUN ARID TWITHLEMMON
LEST EEL HALSEY OATS

Taking Note

MASC SLO RAJ SONAR
ACTA POUF SOLO CAMINO
CARRYOUTOROBEY AGENDA
EDITOR PREFIXFORAGAIN
NIUE EGEAN UPONA
WAGER ADE BLIN WAR
ABBREVIATEDMILE ACARE
TEE ILL DIARY TRAINS
ELAPSES AGARD DEEPSET
RENEE ALEC REROUTES
SCOTTISHFORFALL
ARTERIAL ROSS AESIR
NEATEST PRONE FORTUNE
TUBATE MOUND KIN PAM
ANOSE MONEYUSEDINPERU
EER FUND TRE ORRIS
BEAST ASIAN ATIC
AFRENCHARTICLE SENARY
PLATTE NEWZEALANDTREE
TENTED ALAE GENE EGAN
SATYR SYR DAR RODS

Stepquote

EVERYR THOMAS REGATTA
RAPPEE RAVISH ANOTHER
ONEILL AVERSE CANTERS
IDI PIGGERY TWIT NAME
CARA GLINT PLANET GIN
ALAR IOOS TRADE HYENA
DROWN PAINE TEAOIL
STEEN BAKED THIEF
JOHNNIE LIED THOR RCA
EVENEST ANT SIR TEAL
HIRE GOODTHATTEA HATE
OTIS IKE ETO ACHESON
LEG BALE SCAN THISONE
HALLE MEANY ELENA
ARTFUL LANKY PASTA
GESTE CANOE DOOM OPAL
EGO RHETOR LORNA FORE
LEFT ALEF CONTENT MIA
ENMASSE WAHINE TAKEON
SCARRER ADORER ORELSE
SYNTONY ROWERS BEGOOD

Cryptic Crossword

COUNTERCHARGES
R O L H R R U
INDISPOSE SLEEP
M I T P L O C P
PANDA ESSENTIAL
R A L R E A E
OBLIGES ANTONYM
V I E E
ICECAPS ABSTAIN
S G T R T R T
AMORPHOUS DICTA
T T A I E R H R
IDIOT CANDIDACY
O S E A I V I
NATURALSCIENCE

Country Life

ADELAS ELMAN FLAT
SHOREUP LEAVES FLOURS
CONGOLESETREES LASSIE
AMO DETAINS TAU ETRE
TERSE DON ITA STIRRED
WPA KOREANLIEN AMY
ANAIS ERA IAN COLE
BRONCOS ISTLE BALI
ACRE POINTE TIO GAR
SAWER ANTWERP CLEANED
ADE HAITIANRATION ALE
LEGHORN STOOLIE GALEA
SIA USO EGRESS VIAL
ALAN TORSI TINIEST
INON SIC SAC DEANE
TML DUTCHHUTCH OAR
OPERATE SOV EAU TYROL
RAGA INK GUSTING ETE
TRINAL ITALIANGALLEON
STOGIE DYNAST ETOILES
SNED ESSIE REMISS

Across

1 COUNTERCHARGES (pun)
9 IN + DIS + POSE (char. + rev.)
10 SLEEP (rev.)
11 PANDA (homo.)
12 ESSENTIAL (anag.)
13 O + BLIG~~H~~ + ES (char. + dele.)
14 A(N(TON)Y)M (double cont.)
16 I + C + ECAPS (char. + rev.)
19 ABS + TAIN (char. + anag.)
21 AMOR(PH)OUS (cont.)
23 DIC(T)A (rev. + cont.)
24 IDIOT (hid. rev.)
25 CAND(I + DAC)Y (cont. + char. + rev.)
26 NAT(URALS)C + IENCE (cont. + char. + anag.)

Down

2 OR(DIN)AL (cont.)
3 NOSTALGIA (anag. & lit.)
4 ELO + PER + S (rev. + char.)
5 CHE + L + SEA (char.)
6 ~~P~~ARSON (dele.)
7 GR(E)CIAN (anag. + cont.)
8 SUPPLE + MEN + TAR + Y (char.)
9 I'M + PROVIS(A + T)ION (char. + cont.)
15 TE(S)T DRIVE (anag. + cont.)
17 EGOTIS + T (anag. + dele. + char.)
18 S + TOI(CA)L (char. + cont.)
19 ARSENIC (hid. rev.)
20 ARCH + AIC (char. + rev.)
22 PATE + R (char.)

Sight and Sound

STS REGNI HADNT MUG
LOW EGOISM OBEAHS ENE
ONE WATCHYOURSTEP ADS
WEEVIL KONAS CARESNOT
TORIC TATES LACTI
MAGNETOS SETH GIANTS
ARI DENTS ROOST ERGOT
TERR TEMA POOHS SLUR
SALEM EWELL SPEAK EPI
AMAN LOAD BLESSED
AIRLIFT LAPOF OVERSEE
PREMIUM FARO TENT
POD ISEND ZILCH SARDI
ENAS SNOWS CIAO SEEN
AINTS THATS ORFEO PEG
REDEEM ROMP PUNCTURE
BALED FRERE STEEL
BALLETIC MEARA RANSOM
ORA CHARLESDILLON IDO
ENC TONIER OCTOPI VET
ROK DEBTS SONYA EAT

Kitty Litter

ABAS USDA MOOG APTEST
CENT SOON ATNO TOOTOO
TAKEMEOWTOTHEBALLGAME
STAROF DEL EDIT IOTAS
NOUS NITR OSS
ABBE LIONDOWNONTHEJOB
SOURS NRA RADNER LUCE
KIN UBIE SOYAS SLIER
ESCAPECLAWS KISSMECAT
REOPEN GAEA THEE ENS
TROUPER TREACLE
ABA MILL MATE ALLEGE
DANRATTER MISSINGLYNX
ENDON AURIC ANTA DAM
ETES FASTON STO SPIRE
PUSSCOMESTOSHOVE REST
AXE ARTE OLGA
TRIER BEST ABE ELLICE
MANXOFATHOUSANDVOICES
ANGELA CORP NODE NARC
NIECES HOYA GLEN ERTE

Ups and Downs

Saints Alive!

Brief Encounters

AVID ABS PRIZE HIGH
WIRE IRE BROKEN COMAE
ANALYSIS REMORA APPLE
YES ALMANAC NOB SPEED
COLE MACAWS LAKER
ALINE PETERI RED MAS
LOBE SOS RINSE AFRAME
PULSATE DOODAD MAENAD
STE TEMPO UPPER BLEDA
UMP ROSSI PES INON
TRANSITORY PROSPECTUS
RIBS NEV SMEAR EAT
AMBER LIETO STARS ERA
MORASS DRENCH CREEPER
PSETTA ELMER BUY CHIC
SEV GBS IMARET SHEDS
IDLER SCENIC BOOM
FLARE AMO REMOVER EPI
LATEN VENDOR METEORIC
ANEST ODIOUS ERE KALE
WEDS SECTS SAL SLED

Typecasting

ROTA TREAT DAKAR CAMP
ICON HORSE EMILE OLIO
THEDRESSER BODYDOUBLE
ASSAILS ARCUS SUNROOM
NCO ION CAT
MATTERS REEKS GENETIC
ASHE DATER STEED DHAL
ICE DAB ANN EMU
NABS FIRESTARTER ITBE
EPICURE CHOSE TARSHIS
GATO ORT DESI
MISNAME BOARS YOGURTS
ILLS MARATHONMAN EDEN
NEE GAS ERN MAE
ODES SLYER DESKS HASA
REPLETE LATER SPOONED
ORR DEB EMS
STOGIES TINAS TEATIME
IAMACAMERA TAXIDRIVER
FRAN KEVIN ELITE LALO
TANS YEAST RESOD ENDS

I.Q. Test

DADA CUPS FIAT ALAW
AMOR ANILL INTOW LUCE
COMMUNIQUE LARUE IAMB
CRISP QUEBECNORDIQUES
AYN ROUE RAH INONU
IRONEDOUT ASI SOFIA
PEQUOT SNUBS QUOTERS
IQUIT DJS PASSUP SMIT
OPEN ODEA SHIEST INA
TWELFTH PIQUETTE NAB
IDEO OFHOURS ANTI
SEL TRAVERSE TURNONA
IRK ADNATE DAFT WEBB
ERIS ETHENE ISO TOMBS
VENTURI ROYCE DURYEA
EDSON QES LAMEDUCKS
PICUL PAR NIBS TAY
PROPERETIQUETTE ORIBI
HERA AROAR MARTINIQUE
YEGG TERNS EMEER CULL
SKYE DOST PERE HELD

Miscellany

UNHEARDOF VICAR GARBO
POURBOIRE ACOMA ETHER
STREETCAR RIPON ATOLL
TIL ROK ROGET CBRADIO
ACIS REGULAR TOO CAEN
GENUS YELLS WARMTH
EDGING LEA BOX BRECHT
TORIES FARAWAY HAH
DISCRETE BACKBAY WARE
ESTATES LUCKILY GILDA
ARISEN SALTINE CONDOR
LAMED HAULING TRIDENT
TESS HANGDOG FIANCEES
ILO CATCHON SLEIGH
NINEAM TAG HUE GUIDES
ALLBUT POSEN PLANE
HALS ELM CRYPTOS LYRA
AGITATE CHUTE UMP CAB
TAKEN WUHAN CAMEOFAGE
EVENT UKASE TREASURED
SENDS PERMS SMARTNESS

Marching Bands

D	E	M	O	N	S	T	R	A	T	E	G	Y
W	A	S	S	A	I	L	A	N	T	H	E	M
O	U	T	S	E	T	S	E	N	E	C	A	N
H	E	A	P	O	R	C	H	E	S	T	R	A
S	I	Z	E	S	H	E	L	L	C	A	T	S
E	L	A	P	S	E	M	I	N	A	R	E	T
D	I	L	U	T	E		G	E	M	I	N	I
I	M	P	A	C	T	A	R	S	E	N	I	C
S	T	A	T	E	L	E	S	S	L	E	N	S
H	A	R	P	O	O	N	S	T	O	O	G	E
S	O	O	N	E	S	T	U	P	T	U	R	N
A	L	F	R	E	D	R	O	S	E	B	U	D
T	O	P	E	K	A	N	S	E	R	I	F	S

Golf Anyone?

AMBLED ATLAS BEANOS
MORALE LEERED EARLOBE
UNITAS ENTIRE BLOATED
ACHIPOFTHEOLDBLOCK
ENOL EEL LOT KING
TAU ENDOR RIB LEA
AXLE DAN SPREADEAGLES
WEEP ESS ATEN EAVE
AINT KEEL RELATE
WATCHTHEBIRDIE BAG
ADITS ENE SBA SABLE
KIT DRIVETODESPAIR
EBOATS GRID AVER
SALA EASE UME INCH
ARCHIEBUNKER SAN LIEU
MIR DUC CANIS PET
BOAS SLO AHA CNUT
THEWEARINOTHEGREEN
AVIATOR ADESTE AFRAID
LINDENS SETTLE NESTLE
INGEST ESSED DRESSY

Square Routes

P	E	S	A	E	R	G	O	L
D	R	L	E	V	A	R	T	A
K	A	E	T	S	E	A	U	N
W	R	E	S	T	L	I	N	G
D	A	P	R	S	A	N	A	I
A	G	A	P	B	U	R	E	S
U	U	A	A	O	G	R	P	S
Q	S	L	R	S	H	O	E	U
S	L	A	T	I	P	A	C	E

Answer Words

1 Pressure
2 Sleep
3 Grease
4 Log
5 Law
6 Rain
7 Travel
8 Steak
9 Wrestling
10 Laugh
11 Pad
12 Issue
13 Pass
14 Bread
15 Rattle
16 Signal
17 All
18 Peanut
19 Sea
20 Quarter
21 Sugar
22 Shoe
23 Hop
24 Squad
25 Trap
26 Pop
27 Capital

Personals

SOME PLATE WOOF
METAL OILED BAGPIPE
MICHAELSCANE ONETRACK
ALOE MISER NANTES ULE
LEN TIEIN LETS FLAG
MADRE DESI CLIO LASTS
OGLERS ENJOIN CURB
EYESOF EDAMS CONCUR
DELES INA GOVERNOR
HOWS DREDGE SAME YIPE
IDI NEROSWOLF OED
FELT BEDS BILLOW ANDS
ILLUSORY DUC IRONS
LITANY MARKS TROPES
ATNO GANNET MOINES
REMUS HARE TEST SCONE
ERST NERD EMOTE RIT
SIC GOLDIE BRINE AMOI
TEATABLE MARILYNSHORN
STOLLEN INANE THOUS
PEER TANGY SAYS

Letter Shifts

ERECT SHOW ABELL PASS
SELAH TONI RELAY ATTA
ONEREBUSONEREBUS LEAN
TOV ANT DRAPED BEARD
EVADING MORN HISS
RATES TOWITTOWIT ESS
ITONLY ROSS ELATE AWE
CER ALAS DREAM TEA
HERACESHERACES EAT
INASNIT WECAN PRATE
KNOTTS LORAN LEASED
OSTEO HAREM SWINGER
ATO PALENDSPALENDS
LOU TONGS HIDE MED
ART ALENE STEP DERIVE
SEN RAWASRAWAS TULIP
OTIS AMID BROMIDE
METED LEGION ALE TEN
ODOR MADELANDMADELAND
ONUS OPINE EROS FENCE
DATE OPTED DUKE TOTED

Puns and Anagrams

MASCOTS SLIMS
MARTINET TORIES
IMMATURE RUSSET
SMOKES RAID SPA
SORE INCA RIAL
UTE PATER BINGE
SHRIEKS ENRAGED
SKI EON
PRESENT PLATERS
REBUS WIELD MEW
OTOE BING FANE
LIN BANC EVENED
ORISON UNDERAGE
GETSON RADIATES
SEEMS STALLER

Purloined Letters

ARE SWAP MANIC CRY
RIA SHADE JOBETH SHIA
INS HOLDTHEPURSE NICK
SKYLARKS ONETO KNACK
ESCORTS BINDS THUG
OOPS FOCI PROM MUD
IMP TINKERTOEVERSTO
ORE WRONGS AARE ROGET
POE RUNES LIRE MAD
ANALYSIS PESO ELIJAH
LISA TOTHEBITTER NANA
SCYTHE ELON WAGGONER
HAD PNIN GIVEA UME
SWEEP VERO ANGERS AIM
LETSLEEPINGDOGS FRA
YEA EYRE ROMY BRAY
ASEA STELE HEADWAY
BLISS STEEP SOFTSHOE
BOOR OFTENTHANNOT IRA
ENVY REEVES SCARY TTS
TEE EMMET ACNE EAT

On the Road

STOPS ASWAN DARLAN
ARNIES STOOGE IDEATES
BEERTOTAKEOUT LOTTERY
RAB TIOGA DETOURAHEAD
ATIT LOI DESERTER
STOLE TARN DIEM BASH
WAD TRY ESU UREY
AFTER PAT DSTN SPREAD
CLERICAL ETAT AGATE
MALODOR LAURA UTE
ENIF XRATEDFILMS RHOS
POA TINEA ANTHERS
AMAIN LOIN STARESAT
RAZZED ASSD MAT OASES
ATOZ IGN CAP GOV
NEVA CATS LAPP EPEES
STRIPPER HUN NUTS
NOVACANCIES NINON NYE
PRORATE RESTAREAIMILE
STEMLET ELOISE SPACED
STEEDS SENNA ABETS